The Six Red Wizards

...and other stories

Bounty
Books

Published in 2014 by Bounty Books,
a division of Octopus Publishing Group Ltd,
Endeavour House,
189 Shaftesbury Avenue,
London WC2H 8JY
www.octopusbooks.co.uk

An Hachette UK Company
www.hachette.co.uk
Enid Blyton ® Text copyright © 2014 Hodder & Stoughton Ltd.
Illustrations copyright © 2014 Octopus Publishing Group Ltd.
Layout copyright © 2014 Octopus Publishing Group Ltd.

Illustrated by Toni Goffe.

ISBN: 978-0-75372-643-3

A CIP catalogue record for this book is available from the
British Library.

Printed and bound in the United Kingdom
by CPI Group (UK) Ltd, Croydon, CR0 4YY

CONTENTS

The Six Red Wizards

Once upon a time there lived six red wizards. They lived in a castle together, and dressed in red cloaks and red pointed hats. Their eyes, however, were as green as the eyes of cats, and it was said that all six wizards could see in the dark.

Their castle stood right in the middle of the town of Mumble, where many merry little folk lived – but since the coming of the wizards, the people of Mumble had not been quite so merry.

They were afraid of the red wizards. They didn't like their children to play near the castle in case their shouts annoyed the wizards. They didn't like to hold dances on the village green in case the wizards came and stopped them. They wished the wizards would go away.

5

But this was just what the six red wizards wouldn't do! They were very comfortable where they were, and as they were planning a great deal of magic in their castle they were not going to disturb themselves for anyone.

Now the wizards had a servant called Fum, an ugly, bad-tempered little creature who had served them for many years.

One day, he made them an apple pie and by mistake he put salt in instead of sugar. This put the six red wizards into a terrible temper.

"Turn him into a slug!" said one.

"Turn him into a toad!" said another.

"Turn him into a worm!" cried a third.

But before any of them could cast their wicked spells, Fum picked up the apple pie and threw it with all his strength at the wizards. The pie spilled all over them, and while they were wiping the apple juice out of their eyes and noses and ears, and picking the pastry out of their long white beards, Fum ran quickly from the room. He climbed the stairs to his tiny

6

bedroom in the attic. Without a moment's hesitation, he pulled out a little suitcase from under his bed and threw his few belongings into it. Then calling to the wizard's cat, of whom he was very fond, Fum disappeared down a narrow secret passageway.

The six red wizards hunted all over the castle for him, but he was gone. Fum, who knew quite well that he would be turned into something quite horrible if

the wizards found him, had left the castle as quickly as he could and had sped off towards the town of Mumble.

Fum reached the town of Mumble and made his way to the big house where the mayor of the town lived. He knocked at the door and asked to see him.

"His Highness will see you in ten minutes," said the butler. Fum was taken into a little room, and there he waited for ten minutes. Then His Highness the Mayor of Mumble came in, looking very grand and important.

But he didn't look so grand and important after he had heard what Fum had to say – for Fum gave away all the wizards' secrets, and frightened the mayor very much.

"The wizards are making a terrible spell," said Fum. "It is almost finished. When this spell is used, a million soldiers will spring from nowhere, and at the wizards' command they will march all through Fairyland, destroying every town. The soldiers cannot be stopped, for no one can kill them. They will banish

8

the King and Queen, and make everyone
their slaves. The wizards themselves will
sit on six red thrones and they will rule
the whole of Fairyland."

"Oh, this is dreadful!" cried the mayor,
his cheeks turning pale. "Are you sure
of this, Fum?"

"Quite," said Fum. "But if you don't
believe me, I will take you into the castle
through a secret passageway, and you
can peep through a hole to see the
wizards at work, making soldiers out of
nothing."

9

So that night the mayor and three of Mumble's bravest men were taken by Fum through a secret passage into the castle. They peeped through a hole in the wall and there, sure enough, they saw one of the wizards standing in a chalk circle. As he chanted magic words, soldiers started to appear out of nowhere. The watchers gasped and stepped back in fear.

The next day the mayor called a meeting and told the townsfolk all he had seen. He sent a message to the King and Queen themselves, and soon all Fairyland was full of fear.

Then the King sent a messenger throughout the land, proclaiming that if anyone could force the wizards to leave the country, he would be made a prince and could marry the King's most beautiful daughter.

Now it so happened that a wandering seller of lamps and candles heard the messenger proclaiming his news. He marvelled to think that almost overnight a man such as he might become a prince

and marry a princess.

The candle-seller continued on his way selling his wares, but he couldn't get the messenger's proclamation out of his mind. One day he came to a pond and looked at himself in the water. He saw a young and merry face looking back at him, with twinkling eyes and black curly hair.

"Now," he said, "why should I not be the man who becomes a prince and wins the lovely Princess for a wife?"

With that he made up his mind to try. He journeyed to Mumble, and soon came to the castle of the six red wizards. He stood looking over the wall, wondering what to do.

"Beware!" said an old woman, coming by. "Over a hundred youths have tried to defeat the wizards this week – and not one of them has succeeded. Do you see the big cage in that window over there, full of birds? Well, the wizards turned each rash youth into a bird, and placed them in the cage. There they will stay for the rest of their lives."

"Well, I am going to try my luck," said the youth, and he knocked boldly at the castle gate. It swung open and he went in, carrying his candles and his lamps with him.

He climbed a long flight of steps up to the castle door, which slowly opened as he approached. He stepped through and found himself in a great hall.

The six red wizards sat in a row at one end. The youth went up to them and bowed.

"Do you wish to buy new lamps or candles?" he asked. "I have come from afar to sell my wares."

"We want no lamps or candles," said one wizard. "But we do need a servant, since our last one ran away. Do you know anything of magic?"

"I have learned a little," said the youth.

"Do you work hard?" asked the second wizard.

"Yes, for I have done nothing else all the days of my life," answered the youth.

"Then you shall be our servant," said the third wizard.

"Wait," said the youth. "I am only used to serving wise and powerful masters. Prove to me first that you are learned in magic, and I will then gladly be your servant."

"Now this is a bold youth to talk so," the fifth wizard said angrily, to his companions.

"Not so," said the sixth. "It is all the better for us if he has been used to powerful masters. He will do our bidding well."

14

"Only if you are clever enough!" said the candle-seller.

The wizards began to laugh among themselves, for never before had they met such a bold young man.

"Very well," said the first one. "We will show you what we can do."

They meant to frighten the youth and make him sorry for his bold words, but it was difficult to make him afraid, for he had one of the bravest hearts in the world. He did not tremble when with one accord the wizards turned into roaring lions, nor did he spring back

when they changed into a raging torrent that rushed around his feet.

Then they changed into spiders and began to weave a web round him – but the youth laughed in scorn. At once they turned into eagles and flapped their wings about his head but still he only smiled.

Last of all the wizards made themselves very small and then suddenly very big – but not a shiver or a tremble could they get from the brave candle-seller.

"Ho!" he said, when the six wizards stood once more in front of him. "That was quite good magic – but I have seen those spells performed at least a hundred times before. Do three things that I command you, and then I will be your servant."

The six wizards frowned.

"What are the three things?" they demanded. "And before you speak, we must warn you to be careful, bold youth. You will perhaps find yourself in the cage with those birds before very long."

"Then you will lose a good servant," said the youth. "Now here are my three tests. First, can you make yourselves invisible?"

The wizards laughed scornfully. They spread out their hands, said a curious magic word, and lo and behold, they had disappeared! Their chairs were empty!

"Very clever!" said the youth as the wizards suddenly appeared again, and sat down in the chairs.

"What is your second test?" they asked.

"The second test is – multiply yourselves by three!" said the youth.

In an instant, instead of the six red wizards, there were eighteen, and they surrounded the youth in a ring. He didn't turn a hair, but waved his hand to tell them to become six again.

"Now your last test," said the wizards.

"Ah!" said the youth. "This last one is a test that only a few wizards can do." And, so saying, he set out six candles in candlesticks on the table.

"Now," said the candle-seller. "Turn yourselves into the six flames of my candles!"

With a scornful laugh the six red wizards disappeared, and immediately six red flames, burning steadily, appeared at the top of the six candles.

"Ha!" said the youth mockingly. "Very clever!" Then, lightly and easily, he blew at each candle in turn. *Puff!* Out went one flame. *Puff!* Out went another. *Puff!* Out went a third. *Puff! Puff! Puff!* Out went the fourth, fifth and sixth – and where were the six wizards? Gone out with the candle-flames! They had had no time to take their own shape again,

18

and they were blown out for good. To this day no one has ever heard of them again.

"Ho-ho!" laughed the youth. "That's the end of the six red wizards! Now this castle is mine and all the treasure in it! Tomorrow I shall be made a prince and the lovely Princess will be mine!"

Then he noticed that the birds in the cage were all clamouring to be set free. He opened the cage door and they flew out. No sooner were they free than each bird became the young man he had been before. They one and all crowded round the youth, and swore to be his faithful servants.

What merry-making there was in the town of Mumble and in the whole of Fairyland that night! The news flew from place to place, and the King and Queen themselves came in great state to see the wonderful youth who had defeated the six powerful wizards.

And next day the wedding bells rang out merrily, for the Princess herself came to marry the youth. When she saw his twinkling eyes and black curly hair she was glad, and smiled at him. He smiled back at his lovely bride, and so with glad hearts they were married, and lived happily ever after.

The Wonderful
Teddy Bear

Once there was a fat little teddy bear who lived in the toy cupboard. He thought rather a lot of himself, especially as he could do several things that he thought were rather clever.

"I can tie a bow," he said. "Look, I can tie your ribbon in your hair, Rosebud. Stand still, and I'll tie it."

He tied quite a nice bow, and talked about it for a whole day.

"I can thread beads, too," he said, when another doll's bead necklace broke. "Angela, I'll thread your necklace again and you can wear it."

So he picked up the beads and threaded them for Angela. She was pleased, but Teddy spoiled it by boasting about the necklace all day long.

"I mended it," he kept saying. "I picked up all the beads. I threaded them on some cotton. I am really very, very clever."

"You would be cleverer if you didn't boast," said the sailor doll. "If you ever mention beads again I shall chase you round and round the table till you fall over. Go over there into the corner and be quiet."

"But why should I be quiet?" asked Teddy. "I like to talk. It would do you a lot of good if you listened to me, Sailor Doll."

"I've gone deaf," said the sailor doll, putting his hands over his ears. "I can't hear you!"

And wasn't it annoying for Teddy when all the other toys giggled and covered their ears up, too!

So, however much Teddy told them about all the clever things he could do, nobody was able to hear him.

Then one day he found a card lying on the floor of the playroom. The children had been playing a game of

22

cards earlier that day and had dropped one of them. Teddy picked it up and looked at the picture on the other side.

Oh, what a fine picture he saw! It was a picture of a fat little teddy bear, dressed in a top hat, a smart bow, and carrying a walking stick! Underneath it were four words:

THE WONDERFUL TEDDY BEAR

"There!" said Teddy in delight. "Here's my picture! My very own picture – and look what it says underneath – 'The Wonderful Teddy Bear'. That's me! Oh, I

must hurry and show it to the other toys!"

So he hurried to show it to Rosebud and Angela and the sailor doll and the clown and the wobbly man and all the rest.

"Look! This is me! Now will you admit how clever and wonderful I am? Look at my top hat – and my beautiful bow! I'm The Wonderful Teddy Bear!"

They all looked.

"But you haven't got a top hat and a walking-stick," said the sailor doll. "And you'd look silly if you had."

"I would not," said Teddy. "And what is more, I think I would look fine with them. I think I ought to have them. I think you ought to buy them for me."

"Well, you can go on thinking," said the sailor doll. "Anyway, that's only a picture."

"But it's a picture of me!" said Teddy. "The Wonderful Teddy Bear! It says so underneath. It's my very own picture, the artist must have meant it for me. He must know me."

24

"Rubbish," said the sailor doll. "I don't believe it."

But Teddy went on and on about his picture. He didn't know it was a playing card. He pinned it up inside the toy-cupboard so that he could look at it all day long, and the other toys got very tired of seeing it stuck there.

And then one day the sailor doll found the whole pack of cards in a box! There they were – cards showing dolls and bears and clowns and all the rest. The sailor doll looked at them very carefully indeed.

He found three more cards showing teddy bears. One showed a teddy bear sitting in a corner, looking very sad. Underneath the picture four words were written:

THE NAUGHTY TEDDY BEAR

Then the sailor doll looked at the next card. It showed a teddy bear stealing some sweets from the toy sweetshop.

Underneath it four words were written again:

THE WICKED TEDDY BEAR

And on the last card was a picture of a teddy bear running away from a little clockwork mouse. Underneath it were four words again:

THE SILLY TEDDY BEAR

Dear me, how the sailor doll giggled. He looked round and saw that the fat little teddy bear was away at the other end of the room, telling the clockwork mouse how brave he was.

The sailor doll took down the picture of The Wonderful Teddy Bear and pinned up the other three instead. Then he sat and waited.

Soon the other toys caught sight of the three cards and they went to have a look at them. How astonished they were!

"Oooh, look – isn't Teddy a coward? – he's being chased by the clockwork mouse – he's very, very silly. And do look – how very shocking, he's stealing sweets out of the toy sweetshop. Ha – no wonder he's called wicked. And in this one he has been put into the corner because he's been bad. That's where we should put him when he makes a nuisance of himself."

Teddy came up. He had got himself a smart bow and a little stick, but he hadn't been able to find a top hat. He swung his stick as he came up. "What are you looking at? My wonderful picture?" he asked, proudly.

"Yes, we're looking at some pictures of you," said the sailor doll, with a giggle. "They're much more like you than the other one you pinned up."

"Oh! Oh! Look at me, chasing him!" cried the clockwork mouse, and he laughed so much that his key fell out.

"And my goodness me – he's stealing sweets," said Rosebud, shocked. "If he does that kind of thing I'll certainly never speak to him again!"

"Let's put him in the corner, like he is

in this picture!" said the sailor doll, trying
to be stern and not giggle.

Teddy stared at the three pictures in
the greatest astonishment and alarm!
Goodness! How had they got there?
Where was the beautiful picture of him in
the top hat and the lovely bow? These
were quite dreadful!

"They're not me!" he cried. "They're
not!"

"But it says they are!" said the clockwork mouse. "And it's the same teddy bear in these pictures as it is in the one you first showed us. It *is* you!"

"Who would have thought Teddy was so bad?" asked the wobbly man, really shocked. "I really do think we ought to put him in the corner."

Teddy crept away on tiptoe to a corner of the playroom. He took off his smart bow, and threw away his walking stick. Then he went back to the toys.

"Please," he said, "if I say that the first picture wasn't me after all, will you say that these aren't me either?"

"You mean that if we don't believe these pictures are of you, you won't believe the one of the wonderful bear is you either?" asked the sailor doll.

"Yes," said Teddy, humbly. "I'm not bad or wicked or silly – but I'm not really wonderful, either. So please do take those pictures away!"

The sailor doll took them down and put them back in the box where he had found them. But he was giggling so much as he put them away that the toy clown begged him to tell him what the joke was.

"Well, turn round and look at the clockwork mouse," said the sailor doll, laughing. "He's chasing Teddy round and round the table! He thinks that one of the pictures is real, anyhow!"

Poor little teddy bear! He never once boasted again, which was a very good thing. But the clockwork mouse chased him so often that in the end the sailor doll had to take his key out.

He does have to keep the toys in order, doesn't he?

The
Lucky Jackdaw

Once upon a time there was a little girl called Fiona, who lived with her aunt and uncle. One day she found a baby jackdaw on the ground. He had fallen from a nest in the church tower, and couldn't fly back.

"You poor little thing!" said Fiona. "I'll take you home and look after you till you're well enough to fly away."

So she took him home and found a cardboard box which she stuffed with hay. She put the little black creature into it and then went to find some bread and milk.

"Good gracious!" said her aunt. "Whatever will you bring into the house next? You brought a stray cat last month, which stole the joint out of the larder. Last week you found a stray dog with a

33

bad leg, and it chased our chickens as soon as it got better. Now you've got a wretched little jackdaw who will steal everything shiny and bright he can lay his beak on, as soon as he can fly!"

"Oh please, Auntie, let me look after him," begged Fiona, who was so kind-hearted that she really couldn't leave any small or hurt creature by itself. "I'll keep him in the shed outside if only you'll let me look after him. I'm sure he'll fly away as soon as he's big enough."

"Very well," grumbled her aunt. "I suppose you can keep it if you like. But if that bird steals any thimbles of mine, I'll punish you, so there!"

So Fiona kept the jackdaw in the shed outside. She had to feed it many times a day, for it was a hungry little thing. She put bread soaked with milk on the end of a pointed stick, and the little creature took it greedily.

Jack grew very quickly, and soon had a pair of strong black wings. But he didn't fly away! He was so fond of Fiona that wherever she went he went too, and even

34

if she went for a walk, the jackdaw flew along with her, circling round her head and calling, "Chack! Chack! Chack! Chack!"

Then he began to be naughty. He went into the house one day and saw Fiona's aunt sewing. She put her bright thimble down for a moment, and Jack caught it up in his beak. In a second he was out of the window, and had hidden the thimble in a hole right up in the thatch.

"Oh, you wicked bird!" cried Fiona's

aunt. "Bring me that thimble back at once! Fiona! Fiona! Where are you? That jackdaw of yours has taken my thimble! I told you that was what would happen!"

Fiona called Jack and made him bring back the silver thimble. Then she scolded him hard, and he sat on the fence and hung his head.

But it didn't make him mend his ways. Whenever he saw anything bright and gleaming he picked it up in his beak and flew off with it. Fiona's aunt was angry, and she said she wouldn't have Jack in her shed if he didn't stop his wicked ways.

Fiona was very miserable. She was fond of Jack, and couldn't bear to think that he might have to leave. Her aunt scolded her, not because she was a nasty lady, but just because she was very worried about a lot of things.

"Your uncle hasn't been able to work for a month because of his bad leg," she said. "And the hens are not laying and the cows are not giving enough milk. Where is the money going to come from

to pay the rent? I really don't know. The
shoemaker wants his bill paid, too. You'll
have to help me a little more, Fiona, to
make up for that horrible bird of yours
always worrying me. I'm sure he took
the money I put on the dresser
yesterday."

Poor Fiona! She worked hard from
morning to night to help her aunt. She
fed the hens and milked the cows, she
looked after her uncle and did everything
she possibly could. She begged her aunt
not to get rid of her jackdaw, but her
aunt wouldn't promise.

"If only the bird would pay you back for your kindness to it!" she said. "If it was a hen it could lay eggs! But it just does nothing but steal things."

Now the jackdaw knew that the aunt hated him, and he was very unhappy. He flew off by himself one day, and came to a buttercup field. He fluttered down to the river that flowed through it, and as he walked down to the water to have a drink something very bright caught his eye.

It was a ring. It lay in the water near the bank, and seemed to wink at him as the stream went rushing over it. Jack thought it was very pretty indeed. He put his head into the water and pulled out the ring.

It shone even more brightly. It had three great big shiny stones in it, and Jack pecked at them. But they were held tightly in the ring, and he could not get them out. So he decided to take the ring back home with him and show it to Fiona.

Off he went. Fiona was sitting peeling potatoes with her aunt, and they were talking together.

"Mr Brown told me this morning that Lady Penelope went out in a boat on the river yesterday and lost her beautiful diamond ring," said Fiona's aunt. "I expect that it will never be seen again. They say it is worth a lot of money."

"Is it worth as much as a hundred pounds?" asked Fiona.

"Oh, the ring will be worth much, much more than that!" said her aunt.

"Why, there's a reward of a hundred pounds offered to anyone who manages to find it."

When Jack heard this he gave such a squawk that Fiona's aunt jumped and dropped her potato knife on the floor.

"There's that horrible bird again!" she said. "I'll have someone take him away tomorrow, I really will!"

Jack squawked again and hopped up to her. He dropped the ring right into her lap and then stood with his head cocked on one side to see what she would do with it.

The woman picked up the diamond ring and looked at it in the greatest astonishment. For a moment she could hardly speak. Then she found her tongue. "Fiona!" she said. "Fiona! I do believe this is the ring that Lady Penelope lost! Your jackdaw must have found it in the river!"

"Oh, Auntie!" cried Fiona in delight. "Then we shall get the hundred pounds! And you can pay the rent and the shoemaker and the doctor, and you'll

have plenty of money left over!"

"Put on your coat and come with me to the house where Lady Penelope lives," said her aunt, in great excitement. So Fiona got her coat and then she and her aunt set out for the big house which belonged to Lady Penelope. Jack went along too, flying round their heads and shouting, "Chack! Chack!" as loudly as he could. And for once Fiona's aunt didn't scold him.

At last they arrived at the house. The butler took them into a big room, and Lady Penelope came in to see them. As soon as she saw the ring she cried out with joy, and took it from Fiona's aunt.

"Wherever did you find it!" she cried. "What part of the river was it in?"

"Our jackdaw found it," said Fiona.

"Chack! Chack!" cried the jackdaw, flying to the window. Lady Penelope thought he really was the cleverest bird she had ever seen.

"I found him when he was a baby," said Fiona. "I looked after him till he was big, but he wouldn't fly away. He stayed with me all the time. Sometimes he is very naughty, but now he really has been very good we shall have to make a fuss of him! You won't want to get rid of him now, will you, Auntie?"

"No," said her aunt. "He really has paid you back for your kindness to him, Fiona!"

"And I must pay you your reward!" said Lady Penelope. "I will send the money this evening when I have been able to get it from the bank."

Off went Fiona and her aunt again, very, very happy, for all their troubles were gone. The jackdaw knew they were glad and he shouted loudly all the way home.

The money came that day. Fiona's aunt paid all her bills, bought some more hens, and a pretty new dress for herself. Fiona had two new dresses, and a pair of pretty blue shoes.

They wanted to give Jack a present, too, but all they could think of was a little bit of nice fresh meat, which he ate greedily.

Fiona's aunt never said another word against him. In fact, she became very fond of him, and after that she always let Fiona look after any stray animal or bird that she found, so the little girl was very happy.

As for Jack, he lives with them still – but if you go to see Fiona, be careful not to leave your money about! He is still very naughty at times!

Mr Twiddle
and the Sweets

Mr Twiddle was very fond of boiled sweets, and he often went to the sweet-shop to buy them. Mrs Twiddle said it wasn't right to be greedy over them, so he usually only bought two pennyworth at a time. There were red, yellow, and green boiled sweets. Mr Twiddle was always hoping there might be blue ones too, but there never were.

Now one day, just as Mr Twiddle was going out to buy himself some of his sweets, Mrs Twiddle came into the kitchen looking very upset.

"Look!" she said. "The lovely necklace that you gave me for my birthday has broken. Come and help me to pick up the beads. They are all over the place."

So Mr Twiddle went into the parlour to

look for the beads. He found some under
the table, some under the sofa, and two
under the bookcase.

"Don't you worry, my dear," he said
to Mrs Twiddle. "Don't you worry! I'll
take your beads to the jeweller, and tell
him to thread them all nicely again for
you on a very strong thread. Then your
necklace will be quite all right again, and
you can wear it every day."

"Oh, thank you, Twiddle," said Mrs
Twiddle, and she put all the pretty
coloured beads into a paper bag. Mr
Twiddle put them into his pocket.

"I'm going out to buy myself some sweets," he said. "I'll leave these beads at the jeweller's on my way back." He went into the hall and put on his mackintosh because it was raining, and then out he trotted, down the garden path and into the street.

He came to the sweetshop and bought himself a bag of boiled sweets. They did look nice. He took one out to suck, though he knew that Mrs Twiddle really didn't like him to eat sweets in the road. Then he put the bag into his mackintosh pocket and went down the street, sucking and humming happily.

When he came to the jeweller's shop he remembered that he had to leave Mrs Twiddle's beads. So in he went. He put his hand into his mackintosh pocket and took out his bag of boiled sweets. He quite thought that they were the beads that his wife had popped into the paper bag. But those were in his coat pocket, if only he had remembered!

"Please will you thread these on a nice strong thread and send them to Mrs

47

Twiddle as soon as they are ready?" said Mr Twiddle to the jeweller.

"Certainly, sir," said the jeweller, and took the bag. Mr Twiddle trotted out of the shop and went home, still sucking the red sweet he had had in his mouth since he left the sweetshop.

When he got home Mrs Twiddle saw him sucking the sweet. "Oh, Twiddle dear," she cried, "don't eat any more sweets, there's a darling! It's nearly tea-time, and I'm giving you toast and treacle."

"How lovely!" said Twiddle, taking off his mackintosh and hanging it up. He put his hand into his coat pocket and took out the bag of beads, which he thought were his sweets. He put them into the drawer of the desk in the parlour and then went to have his tea.

Now the jeweller was really astonished when he opened the paper bag that Twiddle had left with him, and saw inside a collection of rather sticky boiled sweets.

"These aren't beads!" he said. "They

are sweets! How can anyone wear sticky
things like these! Well, well – I suppose
Twiddle has some reason for wanting
such a strange thing. I must make some
holes in them and thread the sweets into
a necklace."

Well, he bored a little hole through the
middle of each boiled sweet, and carefully
threaded them on a good strong thread.
Then he put them into a box, gave them
to his boy to deliver, and went on with his
next job.

The boy went to Mr Twiddle's house, banged on the door, and delivered the box. Mr Twiddle was delighted. He hurried into the kitchen with it, beaming all over his plump face.

"My dear! Here is your necklace back again. Would you believe it! Hasn't the jeweller been quick? Open the box, my dear, and put the necklace on again. It suits you so well."

Mrs Twiddle undid the parcel and opened the little box. She took out the necklace. She stared at it in amazement.

"This isn't my necklace," she said at last. "It's quite pretty – but it isn't mine."

"Perhaps it's one that the jeweller sent for you to wear till your own is ready," said Twiddle. "Put it on, my dear!"

So Mrs Twiddle put it on. But her neck was warm, and the sweets that the necklace was made of were sticky. She began to feel most uncomfortable.

"Oooh!" she said. "This necklace is dreadfully sticky. I don't like it a bit." She took it off and looked at it. Then she gave a little giggle.

"What's the matter?" said Mr Twiddle. Mrs Twiddle passed him the necklace with another little giggle.

"Lick the beads and see if you like the taste," said Mrs Twiddle. Mr Twiddle was astonished. He licked the beads – and they tasted sweet! He looked and looked at them – and then he went very, very red. He was beginning to guess what had happened. He got up and went to the desk. He opened the drawer and took out the paper bag he had put there. He looked inside – and there were his wife's beads! Well, well, well!

"I'm so sorry," said Mr Twiddle in a very small voice. "I must have given the jeweller my boiled sweets to thread. I'm really very sorry. No wonder the necklace felt sticky! Oh dear, to think you've been wearing boiled sweets! Whatever will you do next, Wife?"

"You mean what will you do next, Twiddle!" cried Mrs Twiddle, and she laughed so much that she got hiccups and Mr Twiddle had to undo one of the sweets from the necklace and give it to her to suck.

What a
Good Thing!

"You can all go out for a walk this morning," said Mother to Jean, Harry and Peter. "It's a lovely day."

"Oh, good!" said Jean. "Can we go down to the river, Mum? There may be a few boats out."

"Very well," said Mother. "But just you be very careful so as not to fall in!"

"It's so nice and sunny," said Peter. "I guess we'll be as hot as can be! Need we put our coats on, Mum?"

"Of course you must!" said Mother. "It isn't summer now. And scarves, please! There's a cold north wind blowing, and I certainly don't want you all in bed with colds."

"Oh, Mum! Scarves too! We shall be cooked," said Harry.

"Well, you must be cooked then," said Mother firmly. "Coats, and scarves, please, and no nonsense."

The children were cross about the scarves. They all hated scarves and gloves and wellington boots, and simply would not put them on if they could get out of it.

They went to the cloakroom and took down their coats. Just then the doorbell rang and Jean peeped into the hall to see who it was.

"It's Mrs Jones," she said to the others. "She'll keep Mum talking all morning. We'd better not go and say goodbye, or she'll keep us talking too."

"We can all slip out of the back way then," said Harry. "Come on everyone!"

"I say – as Mum won't see us go, shall we forget to put our scarves on?" said naughty Peter. "It's so hot."

"It is hot," said Harry. "We really shall be cooked in them. But Mum did say we were to put them on."

"But she won't know if we don't," said Peter.

"Peter, don't be so perfectly horrid!"

said Jean. "You know Mum trusts us to do what she says. I call that downright deceitful. It's just simply dreadful of you! Anyone would think you didn't love Mum when you talk like that."

"Well, I do," said Peter sulkily.

"You'd better show it then," said Jean, tying her long woollen scarf firmly round her neck. Harry tied his scarf on too, looking rather red. Peter stood sulkily in the cloakroom. The others didn't wait for him. They ran out into the garden and made their way to the gate that led into the lane.

After a minute Peter joined them. Harry and Jean looked at his neck. He had tied his scarf round just as they had. Jean was glad. It made her angry and unhappy when Peter was deceitful. She took his arm.

"Good old Peter!" she said. But Peter was still rather sulky and he shook off Jean's arm. So she let him walk by himself and ran on ahead with Harry.

They soon came to the river. There had been a lot of rain and the river was swollen and ran very fast. The children threw bits of stick into it and watched them whirl away.

Soon they met George and Mary, and began to play games with them. George had a ball, and the children stood in a ring and threw the ball to one another. If somebody missed, they had to kneel on one knee. If they missed again, they had to kneel on both knees. It was such great fun!

Suddenly the ball went crooked and Mary couldn't catch it. It rolled away and away – right to the edge of the river.

Mary raced after it, afraid it would roll right into the water.

But it didn't. It stopped just at the edge. Mary stooped to pick it up and caught her foot on a root. She fell – rolled down the bank – and *splash!* There she was in the river.

George gave a scream.

"Mary can't swim! Mary can't swim! Quick, oh do come and save her!"

The four frightened children raced to the river and looked down into the water.

Mary had been swept out a little way, and had caught hold of an old branch that had fallen into the bed of the river and stuck there. It just saved her from being swept right away with the current.

"Save me, save me!" cried Mary. "This branch won't last very long. It's cracking already!"

"If only we had a rope!" cried Harry in despair. "How can we save Mary? There's no one about. Oh, what shall we do? What shall we do?"

The branch that Mary was clinging to gave a loud crack. Mary screamed.

"Quick! Quick! The river is taking me away. The branch is breaking!"

"Jean! Harry! Take off your scarves and give them to me!" cried Peter, suddenly, tearing his own scarf off his neck. "Quick! I'm going to knot them together – and then I think they will just reach Mary."

The three children tore off their long woollen scarves. Peter knotted them all together quickly and tightly. Then, with the other children holding on tightly to

his waist so that he should not fall in, he bent over the bank and swung the scarf-rope right out over the river to poor Mary.

Crack! The branch broke in two. The little girl was swept away – but she just managed to snatch at the scarf-rope. She held on as tightly as she could – and Peter held on too.

"Hold tight, hold tight!" he yelled. "I'll pull you in. But do hold tight. The scarves are very strong."

With the others holding him fast, the little boy pulled hard at the scarf-rope. Slowly Mary came nearer the bank. At last she reached it. Peter lay flat and reached his hands to her. She was pulled up to the grass above, dripping wet, frightened and cold – but safe!

"Oh, thank you, Peter!" sobbed Mary.

Even George was crying, for he had been very frightened. "You are so clever! However did you think of making a rope with those scarves? Oh, Peter – just suppose we hadn't worn our scarves today!"

"We almost didn't," said Peter in a small voice. "I think I was rather mean about it – but I'm jolly glad I did just what Mum said now!"

"So are we!" cried Harry and Jean, and they both gave Peter a big hug. "Come on, Mary – you must get home straightaway and be dried."

So off they all went – and, you know, they never forgot that they saved Mary's life by obeying their mother that morning. You simply never know, do you!

The
Remarkable Tail

One day the toad who lived under the old mossy stone crawled out to have a drink from the water nearby. He was a wise old fellow, and nobody knew how long he had lived under his stone. No one dared to take the hole he lived in, for it belonged to the toad.

As the toad slid into the water, a perky little creature swam up to him.

"Hello, Toad! How are you?"

"Good morning," said the toad, swimming away. "And goodbye!"

"Ho! You think yourself very high and mighty, don't you?" said the long-tailed creature, swimming along by the toad. "I've heard all about you – but *I* don't think you are very wonderful!"

The toad turned to look at this cheeky

creature. It was a newt in his spring dress. He had a fine wavy crest all down his back, and a long, graceful tail. Underneath he shone brightly with a beautiful orange colour.

"Go away," said the toad.

"But I want to talk like you," said the newt. "Why does everyone think you are so wise? You don't look it! I think you are an ugly creature! You have no graceful tail as I have! And look at my beautiful orange tummy!"

"I don't want to," said the toad. "It looks like one of those horrid-smelling toadstools that grow in the woods in autumn."

"I do think you look odd without a tail!" said the cheeky newt. "Why don't you try and grow one?"

"Why should I?" said the toad. "I am a wise toad, not a foolish newt like you!"

With that he turned and swam to the edge of the pond. He crawled out and went back to his stone, thinking angrily of the newt. "He will come to a bad end!" thought the old toad. "Foolish young creature!"

The newt was very proud of having talked to the toad. He told everyone about it. "I showed him my tail, and my lovely orange colouring," he said. "And I waved my crest at him and told him he was an ugly fellow! He swam back to the bank feeling very sorry for himself, I can tell you! Oh, I am a grand fellow, I am! When I'm as old as that toad I shall be twice as wise as he is!"

The newt often used to leave the pond

and go to the stone where the toad lived. This annoyed the toad, who liked to be alone. Besides, the newt liked flies for dinner, and was delighted to feast on caterpillars – and the toad liked these things very much too.

"Go away!" he said to the newt. "You are a cheeky youngster, and will come to a bad end. You are foolish to leave the pond like this and come wandering up here. I am safe under my stone. You have no shelter and can easily be seen!"

"Fiddlesticks!" said the newt. "I am no coward like you! Who will catch me, I should like to know? I am on the lookout for any rat, or snake, or stoat!"

Sure enough, when the quiet rat came running up behind the newt, the little

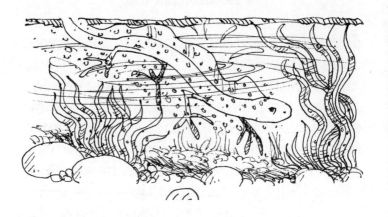

creature heard him, and at once slid through the grass to the water. *Plop!* He was in the pond at once!

Another time the grass snake glided up and the newt shot off just in time. The toad heard the splash as he leaped into the pond. The snake wondered whether to swim after him or not, but decided to look under the stone and see if anyone was hiding there. But when he saw the old toad he drew back his head hurriedly. He had once struck at a toad and tried to swallow him – and the creature had covered himself with such an evil-tasting liquid that the snake had spat him out in disgust. No! Toads were not good to eat.

"Didn't I tell you that I could always escape my enemies?" said the newt, running up to the toad's stone again, as soon as the snake had gone. "You are slow, Toad, but I am quick. You can only crawl – but I can run. Don't you think my tail looks extra well today? The crest goes all the way down to the end. I have been told that I am the prettiest creature in the pond."

"Well, you are certainly the most talkative," said the toad. "I am tired of you. For the twentieth time, Newt, go away, and find someone who likes listening to you. I do NOT!"

"I shall stay here," said the newt. "It is nice and comfortable here, and the sun is warm."

The toad said nothing more. He sat at the entrance to his hole and blinked. Then he saw something that made him stare upwards. A great bird was flying down to the pond. What a big bird it was! It flapped its huge wings so slowly, and trailed its long legs behind it.

"A heron!" thought the toad. "Ha! He

is going to fish in the pond for frogs, newts or fish! He will see this silly newt – and that will be the end of him!"

But the toad was kind-hearted, and he called to the curled-up newt, "Go back to the pond! The heron is coming!"

"I don't believe you!" said the newt. "You are only saying that to get rid of me!"

The heron flew lower – and the newt suddenly saw the shadow of the great wings above him. In terror he tried to run away – but the heron landed beside him, thrust downwards with his strong beak, and stabbed at his tail. Then he picked up the newt by the tail, and was about to swallow him, when the toad called out loudly, "Break off your tail! Break off your tail!"

The frightened newt wriggled and snapped his long, graceful tail right off. He left it in the heron's mouth and fell down into the water. He used his little feet to swim along, and disappeared into a hole in the bank, tailless, scared – but safe!

The heron said, "Kronk!" in a deep voice, and flew off. The newt's tail was not much of a dinner – but the heron knew of another pond that was swarming with frogs!

The toad crept out from his stone and went to the pond. He slipped into it and swam about until he found the hole in which the newt was hidden.

"Are you safe?" he croaked.

"Yes – but I have lost my beautiful tail," said the newt, sadly. "Still, I am grateful to you for telling me of that trick."

"I saw a lizard play that trick on a rat once," said the toad. "Your tail will grow again."

He swam off and went back to his hole.

"That newt needed a lesson," he said to himself. "Now he has got it. Perhaps he will be a wiser newt in future."

The toad saw no more of the newt for many months – and then one day he saw him again outside his stone.

"Good day, Toad," said the newt, in a humble voice. "I have not come to worry you – only to say that my tail has grown again, though it is not nearly so nice as it was before – and I am wiser now, and no longer think I am the most wonderful creature in the pond."

The toad crept out from under his stone and looked at the newt. Certainly his tail had grown – but what a stumpy one compared to his other!

"You may not be so beautiful now, but you are certainly nicer," said the toad. "Come and see me as often as you like. I think that we will be friends now!"

And now you may often see the newt talking to the toad by his stone. You will know him by his stumpy tail. Wasn't it lucky for him that the toad taught him the trick of breaking off his tail? No wonder he is grateful!

The
Dancing Doll

There was once a little dancing doll who lived on the windowsill of Mary's playroom. She was the prettiest little thing, with a key in her back. When she was wound up she would put out her arms this way and that, and dance round and round on her small feet.

As she lived on the windowsill she had no friends among the toys, who all lived together in the playroom cupboard. But she had one very good friend – and that was the blackbird who had a nest in the apple-tree outside. He had a wife, and they had brought up three fine youngsters in their cosy nest. The dancing doll could see them from the windowsill, and loved to watch them.

The blackbird was very fond of the

dancing doll, because she had helped him
to win his wife that spring. There had
been another blackbird in the garden,
and both had wanted to marry the dark
brown hen bird. She could not make up
her mind – and first she looked at one
and then she looked at the other! Which
one should she marry?

The blackbird who was friendly with
the dancing doll had gone to the apple-
tree, and had moped miserably. The doll
had seen him, and called to him to know
what was the matter. When she heard
his tale, she smiled at him.

"I will make you very beautiful and shiny," she said. "Then the hen will think you are lovely, and will marry you – and you can build your nest in this tree so that I may watch you, for I am sometimes lonely sitting on my windowsill here, away from all the other toys."

The blackbird hopped on to the sill. The doll lifted up the window seat, and got out from the cupboard underneath a duster and a tin of polish which Mother kept there. She put some polish on the duster, and then rubbed the blackbird's beak hard. Soon it began to shine and gleam a bright orange-gold, beautiful to see!

Then the doll lifted up the seat again and took out some of the black shoe polish that Father used for cleaning Mary's shoes. She put some on the duster, and began to polish the blackbird's black coat.

You should have seen it when she had finished! It was as bright as a mirror! Off he flew in delight, and when the hen saw his beautiful glossy coat, and heard the glad song he sang from his gleaming golden beak, she fell in love with him at once, and married him.

So you can guess that the little doll was great friends with the blackbird.

"Some day I will do you a good turn too," promised the blackbird. And that day came, as you will hear.

One morning the blackbird found the dancing doll in tears on the windowsill. "What is the matter?" he asked.

"A horrid great bird came this morning and took away my nice shining key," sobbed the doll. "Now I cannot be wound up, so I shall never dance again. I am so very unhappy."

"What sort of bird was it?" asked the blackbird.

"It was a great big bird, all black, except that he had a grey patch at the back of his neck," said the doll. "Oh, blackbird, do you think you can help me?"

"I'll try," said the blackbird. "That bird was a jackdaw. Jackdaws love shiny things, and often steal them and hide them. He may have put your key in his nest for his young ones to play with. I will go and see."

He flew off. He knew where the jackdaw had his nest – high up in the church tower. He flew up and up and at last came to the tower. He perched on the edge of the tower and looked inside it. Sure enough, there was the jackdaw's nest. He had almost filled up the tower with sticks, and in the middle of them he had built his big nest!

"Good morning," said the blackbird. "Come up here and talk to me."

The jackdaw flew off his nest and perched beside the blackbird, always

76

ready for a chat. The blackbird saw the
gleam of something shiny in the nest,
and he knew that the doll's key was
there!

"How are your young ones getting on?"
asked the blackbird.

"Very well," said the jackdaw, "but
they are always so hungry that I find it
quite difficult to feed them."

"I know where there are some lovely,
fat, juicy caterpillars," said the blackbird.

"Oh, do tell me," begged the jackdaw
eagerly.

"What will you give me if I do?" asked the blackbird.

"I have nothing to give you," said the jackdaw. "Well – I only have a little shining thing, of no use to anyone."

"I will have that, I think," said the blackbird. So the jackdaw hopped down to his nest, and picked up the key in his beak. He gave it to the blackbird.

"The caterpillars are in the nettles at the end of the turnip field," said the blackbird, and flew off at once with the key, afraid that the jackdaw might change his mind at any moment!

He flew down to the windowsill, and the doll gave a squeal of delight when she saw her key in his bright beak.

"Oh, you are a darling!" she said. "You really are!"

"I know where there is a piece of string," said the clever blackbird. "I will get it – and then you can tie the key to yourself, Dancing Doll – so that if the jackdaw comes again, he will not be able to take it away!"

He wound up the doll – and she danced

merrily for him. Then off he flew to get
the string. And now the key is tied tightly
to the doll, so that the jackdaw will not be
able to get it any more.

"It is nice to have a friend!" said the
doll, hugging the blackbird. And, do you
know, she was quite right!

79

Mr Pippin's Lemonade

It was a very hot day and Mr Pippin was fast asleep in the garden, when his wife woke him up.

"Pippin, Pippin!" she called. "Where are you? I've made some lovely lemonade, and I want you to take it to the market and sell it all to the passers-by for ten-pence a cup. It is such a hot day that folks will buy a lot, and then we shall have a chance to make ourselves some money."

Mr Pippin didn't want to walk to the market on a hot day one little bit. But he knew he would have to, so he got up, and took the big can of lemonade from his wife. She gave him a lot of little cups, and ran a string through their handles so that he would be able to carry them all easily over his shoulder. Off he went to the market.

Now on the way he tasted the lemonade, and he thought it was very good.

"My!" said Mr Pippin. "That really is splendid lemonade, I shall easily sell the lot. I should think there is quite enough in the can to fill forty cups. That means forty tenpence pieces, which is four pounds. Ha! That's a lot of money."

Mr Pippin became really quite excited.

"If I had four pounds I would be able to buy some of Mrs Biscuit's buns, which are only fivepence each, put some jam

in the middle and then sell them for ten-pence each," he said to himself, walking along just as fast as he could.

"Oooh! Eighty buns would put eight pounds into my pocket. I should buy a hen to lay eggs. The eggs would hatch out into chicks, and I could sell them all. I should soon have quite enough money to buy myself a goat."

He was so excited at the thought of having a goat of his own that he stopped quite still.

"A goat. Why, I could sell its milk and make a great deal of money – enough to buy a sheep, perhaps. Think of having a nice woolly sheep. It could feed in the field behind my cottage, and each year it would give me plenty of wool. Soon I should get enough money from my wool to buy a horse. That could live in the field too. I would let the farmers borrow it for ten pounds a day. They would be sure to pay that much for a good horse like mine. How rich I should be."

On and on he walked, and soon he could see the market in the distance. He

was glad, because his can of lemonade was getting very heavy.

"When I am rich I will never, ever walk to market again," he said. "I will ride in my carriage and I shall get a brand new coat for myself and a new hat."

He was so pleased that he skipped a few steps, and some of the lemonade in the can flew out, splashing away into the road.

"I shall buy a fine new cottage too," he

said. "My own is so damp, and it has only two small rooms. Oh, shan't I be grand! I shall walk with my head held high in the air, and I shall order everyone about and tell them just what to do."

Mr Pippin felt so grand that he didn't look where he was going, and he very nearly fell into the ditch. That frightened him, and he walked slowly to the market, looking carefully where he was going, in case he should spill any more of his lemonade.

At last he got to the market, and he sat down on the kerb, by his can of lemonade. He was so excited with thinking of all the grand plans he had made that his cheeks were as red as fire and his eyes were shining bright.

"You look very, very happy today, Pippin!" said Mrs String, the farmer's wife. "Have you found some money somewhere or something like that?"

"No," said Mr Pippin, "I'm going to be very rich, that's why I'm happy."

"How are you going to be rich?" asked Mrs String, who didn't believe that a lazy fellow like Pippin would ever earn any money.

"Well, I shall sell this lemonade, and with it I shall buy some of Mrs Biscuit's buns, which I'll sell for tenpence each, with jam in," said Mr Pippin, excited. "Then I'll buy a hen who can lay me some eggs, and when they hatch out I'll sell them and buy a goat. Oh! I'll soon be rich."

Dame Wimple and Farmer Slap came up to hear Mr Pippin talking. They smiled when they heard him talking about being rich.

"Ho! You may well smile," cried Mr Pippin. "I shall sell my goat's milk and buy a sheep and sell its wool and buy a horse. And I'll hire out my horse to you, Farmer Slap, for ten pounds a day."

"I shouldn't pay you one pound!" said Farmer Slap, and he laughed. "You won't get rich, Pippin."

"I will, I will!" cried Mr Pippin, and he grew red in the face again. "Oh, I'll be very grand indeed. I'll buy a new coat and a new hat, and a carriage to drive about in. And I'll buy a new cottage, and I'll buy a great big dog."

"Whatever for?" asked Farmer Slap.

"To set loose when you come to see me," cried Mr Pippin angrily. "Yes, that will make you frightened all right! I'll turn him loose as soon as you get inside my gate, and he will rush at you barking as loudly as he can. And you'll run away and try your best to dodge him, like this."

Mr Pippin pretended that a dog was after him, and he dodged from side to side, pretending to be very much frightened.

But, alas, he didn't look where he was
going, and he stepped right into his can
of lemonade! Over it went and Mr Pippin
went with it! He was completely soaked
in the sticky lemonade, and a very sorry
sight he looked when he sat up.

"Oh, oh!" he groaned. "There goes my lemonade – and my buns – and my hen and eggs – and my goat – and my sheep – and my horse – and my new coat and hat – and my carriage. Boo-hoo-hoo-hoo!"

"You shouldn't have been so spiteful as to set your imaginary dog on me!" said Farmer Slap, laughing. "It serves you right!"

Poor Mr Pippin! I feel quite sorry for him, don't you?

The
Silly Monkey

There was once a handsome toy monkey who was very proud of himself. He wore a red coat and blue trousers, and round his neck was a very fine yellow scarf that tied in a big bow in front. He was very vain about this scarf, and was always asking the other toys if it looked really nice.

"Oh, do be quiet," the teddy bear would say crossly. "That's the third time you've asked me the same silly question today! You don't deserve such a nice scarf if you're so vain about it! One of these days you'll lose it and that will serve you right."

"Lose it!" said Monkey, scornfully. "You don't know what you're talking about, Teddy! Why, it's tied in a tight bow round

89

my neck, and there's a pin in the front to keep it straight. Don't you think it's a perfectly beautiful scarf, and that it suits me very well indeed?"

"There you go again!" said Teddy impatiently. "That's the fourth time you've asked me. Now, do be quiet."

Monkey left him and went to look at himself in the mirror that was in the doll's-house. He patted his red coat, smoothed down his blue trousers and then admired his beautiful yellow scarf for the hundredth time. He thought he must be the best-looking and best-dressed monkey in the whole world!

Now that night the toys held a tea party in the doll's-house. The curly-haired doll laid the table and set out the little white and blue cups. Then Teddy brought some tiny jam sandwiches and little chocolate cakes. The clockwork clown made the tea, and everything was ready.

At the last minute the clown found that there were not enough cups. Someone would have to go without. As all

90

the toys were feeling annoyed with Monkey and his vain ways, they said he could go without his tea.

"It's just as well!" said Teddy with a grin. "You might spill some tea down that beautiful scarf of yours, you know, Monkey!"

"I'm going to have some tea to drink," said the monkey crossly, hating to be left out.

"Well, there's no cup for you," said the curly-haired doll, busy handing round the cakes and sandwiches.

"Then I shall find a cup for myself," Monkey said angrily and he rushed off. What do you think he had thought of? It was the silver thimble out of Lucy's little workbasket! Lucy was the little girl they belonged to and the monkey thought her thimble would make a splendid cup, far better than the little china ones that the other toys were drinking from.

But when Teddy saw what Monkey was doing, he called out to him at once.

"Monkey! You mustn't take things out of Lucy's basket! She would be very cross

with you! You can't have her little silver thimble!"

"Oh, can't I!" said the silly monkey, and he made a rude face at the bear. "Well, I can, so there! Here it is, see! And I'm going to pour myself out a cup of tea and drink it from this dear little thimble!"

He took hold of the teapot and poured some tea into the thimble. The toys watched him in dismay. It really was very naughty of Monkey, for none of them were allowed to meddle with Lucy's things. All the toys were very fond of her.

Now, just as Monkey was walking to his seat, feeling very pleased with himself, his head held high, he caught his foot in a corner of the rug. Over he went, *smack*! The little thimble of tea spilled on the floor, and the thimble itself rolled right away!

"Ooh! Ow! I've hurt myself!" wept Monkey, rubbing his knee.

"It serves you right," said the curly-haired doll. "You should look where you are going. If you will walk with your head in the air, you must expect to fall over."

"Where's the thimble?" asked Monkey, getting up. He looked around for it but he couldn't see it. "Did anyone see where it went?" he asked anxiously. But nobody had.

"I think it rolled into that corner over there," said the teddy bear, pointing. So the monkey ran to look. But all he found was a hole in the floorboards! And oh, dear me, shining beneath the boards was the little thimble! It had rolled down the hole and there it was.

Monkey tried to get it, but he couldn't. It was too far down. Whatever could he do?

"I can't reach it," he said, half crying. "Teddy, come and see if you can get it."

But none of the toys could reach it. They stood round the hole and looked down at the little thimble, wondering what on earth they could do.

"Lucy will be very upset when she finds her nice little silver thimble is gone," said the curly-haired doll. "It was very naughty of you to take it, Monkey."

"I must get it back, I must!" cried Monkey. "Oh, whatever shall I do?"

"Let's call the little brown mouse who lives behind the wall over there," said the clockwork clown. "Perhaps he will be able to get it for us."

So they called him and he came, his bright black eyes shining and his little nose moving up and down. They showed him where the thimble was, down the hole.

"Can you get it?" Monkey asked.

"Easily," said the brown mouse. "There's a little tunnel that leads from my own hole to this one, and I can get the thimble in my mouth, carry it to my hole and then bring it out to you."

"Oh, please go and get it!" cried Monkey at once, delighted.

"But what will you give me, if I do?" asked the mouse.

"Anything, anything!" said the monkey, looking round. "The doll's pretty brooch – the key belonging to the clockwork clown – the bonnet off the baby doll."

"I don't want any of those," said the brown mouse, looking at the monkey. "I want something belonging to you."

"What's that?" asked Monkey.

"I'd like that yellow scarf of yours," said the little mouse. "I could use it to make a lovely nest for my family. It would help keep us warm all winter. Will you give it to me?"

"Certainly not!" cried Monkey, suddenly in a rage. "Why, my yellow scarf is the most beautiful scarf in the whole world."

"Just right to build a nest with," said the mouse. "Well, if you won't give it to me, I shan't get the thimble for you, so goodbye!"

He ran to his hole – but the other toys surrounded Monkey and spoke angrily to him.

"You were quite ready to give away the doll's pretty brooch and the clown's key!" they cried. "But as soon as something of yours is asked for, you say no! You are a horrible, selfish, vain monkey, and you will give the mouse your yellow scarf!"

The clown suddenly snatched at the yellow scarf and undid it. He dragged it off Monkey's neck and ran to the mouse's hole.

"Little brown mouse!" he called. "Here is the scarf you wanted. Please come and get the thimble for us."

At once the mouse appeared, and took the scarf. He wrapped it round his neck several times and tied the most beautiful bow under his whiskery chin.

He looked too sweet for words, and all the toys smiled to see him. Then he ran down his hole again, found the thimble and brought it safely back. He gave it to the clown, danced round in delight a few times, showing off his fine yellow bow, and then disappeared down the hole to show his family what a wonderful warm nest they would have for the winter.

The clown put the thimble back into the workbasket. He looked at Monkey who was crying in a corner, feeling dreadful without his yellow bow.

"Nobody will like me without my yellow scarf," he groaned.

"Well, nobody liked you with it!" said Teddy. "Cheer up! You won't be vain any more and we will like you lots better."

It was perfectly true – they really did!

When Mr Pink-Whistle
Met the Twins

Mr Pink-Whistle met the twins in rather a peculiar way. He was on his way to Mr Bong's party, and as he was a little late he was in a great hurry. Sooty, his cat, was with him, because he had been invited, too, and they were both going down the street as fast as they could.

"We really must hurry," said Mr Pink-Whistle, hurrying round the corner at top speed. *Bump!* They ran straight into two children, a boy and a girl, and knocked them both right over. Mr Pink-Whistle sat down with a bump, and Sooty rolled into the gutter! Everyone was most surprised.

"Oooh," said the children.

"Good gracious!" said Mr Pink-Whistle,

and Sooty gave a yowl. Mr Pink-Whistle hurried to pick up the two children and was upset to see tears pouring down the little girl's cheek.

"Have I hurt you?" he said. "Oh dear – don't cry so! I'm very, very sorry to have bumped you like that. It was all my fault, I was in such a hurry."

"She's not crying because you knocked her over," said the boy, dusting his sister's coat down with his hand. "She's upset about something else."

"Is she? Why, what's the matter?" asked Mr Pink-Whistle. "You don't either of you look very happy!"

"Well – we don't feel very happy," said the boy. "You see, today we were to have our party, and everything was ready – and then suddenly our granny was taken ill and Mummy had to rush to her house to look after her. So now we can't have our party."

"And we're running to tell our friends not to come," said the girl, rubbing her eyes. "I'm a baby to cry – but I'm so disappointed. We were going to have a conjuror, and we've had to tell him not to come, too."

"What a dreadful thing to happen!" said kind old Mr Pink-Whistle. "I hope your granny will soon be well. I know how disappointed I would feel – I'm just going to a party!"

"Are you?" said the boy. "And the cat, too?"

"Oh, yes. He's been asked as well," said Mr Pink-Whistle. "The funny thing is – it's a conjuror who's giving the party I'm going to! At least, he's a magician, you know – an enchanter."

The twins stared at him in wonder.

What did this funny little man mean? Then the boy saw his pointed ears and caught hold of his sister's arm in excitement.

"Belinda!" he said. "Look – he must be Mr Pink-Whistle. You know – we've read about him! He's the little man who goes about the world putting wrong things right!"

Belinda stopped crying at once, and stared in delight. Mr Pink-Whistle nodded.

"Yes, Pink-Whistle's my name," he said. "What are your names? You're twins, of course?"

103

"Yes. I'm Benny and she's Belinda," said the boy, red with excitement. "Have you put any wrong things right, lately, Mr Pink-Whistle?"

"Not since last week," said Mr Pink-Whistle, "but I'm going to put something right this very afternoon!"

"How? Tell us what it is!" said Belinda, quite forgetting to cry.

"I'm going to take you to the party I'm going to!" said Mr Pink-Whistle. "And all the other children, too! Things went very wrong for you this afternoon, didn't they? Well, I can put them right. Mr Bong, my friend, will be delighted to see you all!"

"But – but will he have enough to eat if we bring about twelve children with us?" said Benny, wondering if he was in a dream.

"My dear boy – haven't I told you he is a magician?" said Mr Pink-Whistle. "One of the very finest I know, too. Now, listen, take Sooty with you and go round to all your friends and ask them to come to Mr Bong's party. Sooty will take you all

104

to Mr Bong's house – and I'll go straight there to warn him I'm bringing a lot more guests! We'll all have a wonderful time!"

The twins could hardly believe their ears. To think that such a thing could happen to them! They set off at once with Sooty, and goodness me, how amazed all their friends were to hear their news! Most of the children were already dressed, ready to go to the twins' party, and it wasn't long before Benny and Belinda had collected them all, and,

with Sooty guiding them, were on their way to Mr Bong's.

They came to a little lane they knew, that led down to the woods – but before they reached the woods, Sooty turned down a trim little path which the children had never seen before.

"You can only see it today because Mr Bong has arranged for it to be here," explained Sooty. "It's a short cut to his house."

And suddenly, in front of them, was

Mr Bong's house! It was really more like a small castle, with towers and turrets – and about a hundred steps led up to a front door that was just below the roof. How strange!

"Isn't it exciting!" whispered Belinda to Benny. "Fancy us not knowing this funny little castle was anywhere near our town!"

Soon they were up the steps and at the front door. Mr Pink-Whistle was there to take them in. They looked round for Mr Bong, but he wasn't there.

"He's coming in a short while," said Mr Pink-Whistle. "Do take off your things. That's right. Now, what are your names? Mr Bong is so pleased you are coming. He has just gone to fetch his own friends."

The children took off their things and Sooty scuttled away with them all. Then suddenly there came the sound of a drum being beaten – *Bom-bom-BOM!* Then a voice cried, "Here comes Bong, the mighty enchanter Bong! Make way for Bong!"

107

The children stared at a great door which had suddenly appeared in the wall. It glittered and shone, and then very slowly it opened.

Through it came a wonderful figure, in a great cloak that glowed like fire. He had a long beard and eyes that shone like lamps. He smiled at all the children.

"Welcome!" he said. "Welcome to my party! Please be friends with my own guests!" He waved his long, shining wand and from behind him came the guests he had been to fetch.

What a mixture they were! "That's Mr Whiskers, a gnome – he's a hundred years old today," whispered Mr Pink-Whistle to the children, as a little man scampered out. "And that's Silky, a fairy from the Faraway Tree. Isn't she lovely? And that's Moonface – he's from the Faraway Tree, too."

"But we know them all!" cried Benny, in delight. "We've read about them in our books! Oh – and there's the old Saucepan Man! Saucepan, Saucepan, can you hear me, or are you deaf today?"

The Saucepan Man beamed round in delight. "I didn't know there were to be children here!" he said, and danced a ridiculous dance, so that all his pans and kettles clanged together and made an odd little tune.

Then a rabbit came in – but what a rabbit! He was dressed very smartly, and grinned round wickedly at everyone.

"Brer Rabbit! Oh, you've come, too!" shouted the children, and ran to him at once.

"Be careful he doesn't play a trick on you," said Mr Pink-Whistle. "Look – here

is a bunch of brownies. They will love to play with you. What about beginning with 'Nuts in May'? Then if others come in late, they can easily join in."

So they began to play "Here we come gathering nuts in May" and when Mr Pink-Whistle and Mr Bong were chosen to pull one another, you should have heard the screams of laughter. In the end Mr Bong won because he poked his wand at Pink-Whistle, and made him only half his size – and then pulled him over easily! More brownies came in, and then three pixies hurried through the door, all as alike as peas – and dear me who was this?

"Big-Ears! It's Big-Ears!" shouted the children and ran to the plump little brownie, who stood beaming round at them. "Where's Noddy? Did you bring him, Big-Ears?"

"No, I'm afraid not. He's taking all the Noah's ark animals to a party," said Big-Ears. "I say, Mr Bong – is it teatime yet? I'm hungry!"

"Yes, yes – we were just waiting for

you!" said Mr Bong. "Sit down at the table, do!"

There was a long table at one end of the room – but there was no food on it at all, only plates and glasses. Everyone sat down.

"Do begin!" said Mr Bong. "Help yourselves!"

"But there's nothing to eat!" said Benny, in surprise.

Mr Pink-Whistle nudged his arm. "Do what the others are doing," he said. "Watch Big-Ears and Silky."

Benny watched. Big-Ears was calling out all kinds of things, holding out his empty hands. "Egg sandwiches!" he cried. "Chocolate eclairs! Pink and yellow jelly! Ice cream – a large one! A glass of iced lemonade!"

And into his hands popped everything he asked for – just like that!

Benny stared and stared. "Good gracious – there's his glass of lemonade!" he said. "It looked as if Big-Ears took it right out of the air! Well – I'll do the same!"

And soon all the children were calling out what they wanted. "Jam tarts! Doughnuts! Tomato sandwiches! A nice ripe peach! Jelly! Trifle! Fruit salad!"

The table was soon loaded with all kinds of good things to eat. Mr Pink-Whistle wasn't very pleased with Sooty, who had called out for fish, and got two rather smelly kippers in front of him.

"Sooty – I've told you before not to ask for fish at these parties," said Mr Pink-Whistle, in a whisper. "Take it under the table, for goodness sake. It smells."

Tea took rather a long time because everyone had rather a lot to eat. Afterwards the children begged Mr Bong to do some magic.

"Shall I spirit you to the moon and back?" he asked, with a twinkle in his eye. "Shall I give you tails like Sooty's? Or would you like wings to fly with?"

"Wings! Wings!" shouted the children, in excitement. They each had to go up to Mr Bong and be touched on the back by his long wand – and wings sprouted there, some like the wings of a butterfly,

113

and some like a bird's. The air was full of flying children, shouting and laughing in joy.

"You may keep your wings to fly home on," said Mr Bong. "But as soon as you fly down to your own doorstep, they will disappear – so make the most of them!"

The magic that the enchanter could do was amazing. He filled the air with the singing of birds – but not a bird was to be seen! He called a rainbow down from the skies – and it slid in at the window, a shimmering, curving bow, so bright that the children could hardly look at it.

Mr Bong took a pair of scissors and snipped pieces from the rainbow, and gave them to the girls. "For you – and you – and you," he said, "to make a new party dress!"

He waved his wand and a small tree grew in the room – a tree that budded as they watched. The buds broke into flowers, which changed into a most peculiar fruit, rather like big brown pears, each with a stalk.

"Pick one each, boys," said Mr Bong.

"You will see what kind of a tree this is then!" So the boys went to pick the strange fruits – and lo and behold, they were spinning-tops and the stalks were the tops' sturdy legs!

"Throw them on the floor," said Mr Bong, and down on the floor went the tops – and there they spun themselves so fast that they could hardly be seen!

"I wish I could grow a top-tree in our garden," said Benny. "These are the best spinning-tops I've ever seen!"

Then Mr Bong grew a balloon bush that budded and then flowered into enormous coloured balloons – and he

grew a cracker tree whose fruits were real crackers. *Pop, bang, pop* they went, when the children pulled them. And what wonderful things fell out of them! There was no end to them.

At last it was time to go. "You can all fly home on your wings," said Mr Pink-Whistle. "Just as Mr Bong said! Take your presents with you – the things out of the crackers, the tops, and the snippets of rainbow, and now – what about a cheer for kind Mr Bong who helped me once more to put a wrong thing right!"

"Hip-hip-hip-HURRAH!" shouted the children and everyone else. "Hip-hip-hip-HURRAH!" And so loudly did they shout that the little castle trembled and shook – and then it vanished into smoke that blew about like a silver mist!

But the children didn't mind! They flew up into the air on their wings, eager to get home and tell their mothers all about the wonderful party. How marvellous to fly like a bird! Mr Pink-Whistle watched them all go, with Sooty beside him. He waved happily.

"I hope they remember that their wings will disappear when they arrive home," he said. "What a time we've had, Sooty – I always enjoy Mr Bong's parties. Dear me – I do hope you will wash your whiskers as soon as you get home, Sooty. You still smell of those kippers!"

Goodbye, Mr Pink-Whistle – and how I hope that if anything goes wrong with me I shall do as the twins did – bump into you round the next corner!

A Surprise
for Jimmy

Jimmy awoke feeling miserable, and he remembered why as soon as he had opened his eyes. It was the school treat and all the children in his class were going down to the seaside for the day.

Jimmy wasn't going. It cost five pounds to go, and his mother said she couldn't possibly pay all that just for a day. Wasn't that a pity? Jimmy looked at the blue sky outside the window and sighed. It was very sunny, with hardly a cloud in the sky. It would be glorious at the seaside.

He went down to breakfast, and afterwards his mother sent him out shopping. As he went down the street he saw an old lady hurrying to catch a bus.

Jimmy saw something fall out of her pocket as she ran. He ran too, then, and picked it up. It was her purse!

"Hey!" called Jimmy. "Hey! You've dropped your purse!"

But the old lady didn't hear him. She clambered onto the bus and away it went, rumbling down the street.

Jimmy looked into the purse. Oh, what a lot of money there was! Wouldn't the old lady be upset when she found that she had lost her purse!

Jimmy looked round for a policeman. He thought he would tell him about it and see what ought to be done. But there was no policemen there.

Jimmy saw another bus coming, and he had an idea. He would get into this bus and go after the old lady. Perhaps he could catch up with her. He would watch the bus in front and see when she got out.

He jumped into the bus and off they went. It was a fast bus and very soon it was not far behind the other bus. Jimmy sat in the front seat and watched to see if the old lady would get out. On they came to the station. Jimmy saw the old lady get out and hurry into the station. Off he jumped too and looked around.

He couldn't see his old lady! Where had she gone? She wasn't buying her ticket anywhere. Perhaps she had it already and had gone to the train.

Jimmy ran through the booking-office, and looked up and down the platforms. There she was! He saw the old lady walking on to the opposite platform from

the bridge that crossed over the line. And, oh dear, there was a train coming in! Would he have time to catch the lady before she went?

Over the bridge he raced and down to the platform. The train was at a standstill there. Jimmy saw that it was a corridor train, with a passage all the way through it from one end to the other, through the carriages. He opened a door and jumped into the passage. Then he began to look into every compartment to find the old lady.

And oh my goodness me, suddenly a whistle blew, and the train started off! Jimmy couldn't open the door in time, and there he was, being carried away by the train! What a dreadful thing! And he hadn't a ticket!

Jimmy stood in the passage and felt frightened. Where was the train going to? He wondered if he dared ask anyone.

As he was standing there, feeling very miserable, he heard a noise in the next compartment. Someone was saying, "Oh dear, oh dear, oh dear!" in a frightened voice.

Then he heard the voice say, "I've lost my purse! Perhaps I have dropped it on the floor. Could somebody look for me, please?"

It must be Jimmy's old lady. He forgot his own troubles, and looked into the compartment. Yes, there she was, looking very worried, and two of the other

passengers were looking on the floor for
the purse. Jimmy pushed back the door
and went in. He held out the little black
purse.

"Here it is!" he said. "You dropped it in
the street when you were running for
the bus."

"Oh, my purse, my purse!" cried the
old lady gladly, and she took it from him.
Then she looked very puzzled.

"But if I dropped it so far away, how did you manage to get here to me?" she asked.

"Well, you see, I got into the next bus and followed you to the station," said Jimmy. "And I saw you were going to catch this train, so I hopped on it to find you. And now the train has taken me with it, and I don't know what to do."

He looked so upset that the old lady was quite upset herself.

"Never mind, never mind," she said. "Come and sit down by me. I'll look after you. This train is going to the seaside, you know. It doesn't stop till it gets there. So you'll have to go to the seaside with it. But what does that matter? We'll telephone your mother to say you are all right, and you shall spend the day with me on the sands. Would you like that?"

Well, would you believe it! Here was Jimmy waking up miserable because he wasn't going to the seaside with the others – and now he was going after all, by mistake. What a very funny thing!

The old lady shared her biscuits with

him on the train. When it arrived at the seaside she phoned Jimmy's mother to say he was all right and she would put him on the train for home after tea. Then off they went to the beach.

What fun they had! The old lady had three grandchildren, who met her at the station, and they took Jimmy down to the sea at once. He paddled and bathed, dug castles, and caught shrimps with a

net – and then the children's mother and granny brought down a lovely lunch for them on the beach.

All afternoon they sailed ships on the pools, and when teatime came they sat on the beach and boiled a kettle for tea. There were jam sandwiches and buns and chocolate cakes, so it was a really lovely tea.

They were all sorry when the time came to take Jimmy to the train. "Come again!" they said. "Come again!"

Their granny paid for his ticket, and kissed him goodbye. "You deserved your treat," she said. "It was kind of you to run after me like that with my purse. You behaved like a little gentleman, and I'm glad you had a day at the sea after all!"

Next day when the school children told Jimmy they were sorry he hadn't gone to the seaside with them, he laughed.

"Oh, I went too," he said. "I didn't mean to go – but I went!" And that did puzzle the children!

The Biscuit
in the Chimney

One afternoon there was a party in the playroom. A lot of children came to tea with Jenny and William, and the toys sat and watched in delight.

"It's a birthday party," whispered Teddy to Sammy, the sailor doll. "William is eight today. Look at all the things they are having to eat."

"That's a birthday cake in the middle of the table," said the big doll, pointing to it.

"It isn't," said the toy dog. "It's got candles on. You don't put candles on cakes."

"You do on birthday cakes," said the big doll. "You're too young to know, Toy Dog. Look – they are lighting them!"

The toys watched in wonder. What a

beautiful cake, with eight glowing candles in a ring! And then, when it was cut, how delicious it looked.

"I wish I could have a piece of it," whispered Teddy. "I've been hungry all day, and now I feel hungrier still."

"There might be some crumbs on the carpet we could have, when the children have gone," said the big doll.

The party went on till half past six and then the children all said "Thank you" and "Goodbye", and went home.

Jenny and William danced back into the playroom with their mother.

"Thank you, it was a lovely party!" said William. "Shall we clear up a bit now, Mummy?"

"Oh no – we'll leave it till tomorrow and then we can do it properly," said his mother. "Now come downstairs and I'll read you both a story before it's time for bed."

So off they went and the toys were able to stand up and look round a bit. Were there any titbits left anywhere?

"I've got a bit of icing off the cake!"

cried the clockwork mouse in delight. "Look! Have a lick, anyone?"

"No – you have it yourself, Mouse," said the big doll. "It's only a small bit."

But the mouse broke it in half and gave a bit to the toy dog. It was delicious!

"I've got a bit of sponge cake – and it's got some jam on it!" shouted Sammy. "We can all share it."

So they each had a crumb and it really was very nice. Then Teddy found a large bit of egg sandwich and he shared that round, too.

Monkey had a good hunt round, but

at first he didn't find anything. And then, quite a long way underneath the table, he saw something long and chocolaty lying on the carpet. Whatever could it be?

He went to see. Goodness! It was a whole chocolate finger biscuit which somebody had dropped. A whole one! Not even nibbled. Monkey could hardly believe his eyes.

Nobody was near him. He picked it up quickly and smelled it. Mmmm! Lovely! He licked it. Ooooh! Delicious! He looked round slyly at the others. If he shared it with them he would only have the tiniest little bit himself. If he didn't share it he could have the whole biscuit to himself. It would last him a very long time.

"The thing is," said Monkey to himself, "the thing is – where shall I hide it? It's so long. I can't put it into the brick-box because the clockwork mouse often sleeps there and he'd smell it. I can't put it into the toy garage because one of the cars might drive into it and break it. Where can I put it?"

He thought hard, sitting in a corner by the wastepaper basket, hidden away from all of the other toys. Then he gave a little squeal.

"I know what I shall do! I'll climb up on the roof of the doll's-house when all of the other toys are asleep – and I'll slip this long chocolate finger biscuit into the chimney. Nobody, nobody will ever guess it's there! I can go and get it out for a nibble whenever I want to."

So he waited till the toys were all asleep, and then he climbed up on the roof of the little doll's-house. He slid the chocolate biscuit into the chimney. Yes, it went in beautifully. He pulled it out and had a nice long nibble at it. What a lovely chocolate biscuit it was!

A little mouse ran out of a hole in the playroom and startled Monkey. He dropped the biscuit down the chimney at once, and then scuttled down and ran over to the toy-cupboard. Nobody must know where that biscuit was hidden!

Monkey was good at keeping secrets. He didn't tell anyone at all about the biscuit in the chimney. But he was so anxious to make sure that it was safe that he kept climbing up on the roof and looking down the chimney. The toys were all very surprised at him.

"Monkey, why do you keep sitting on the roof and looking down the chimney?" asked Teddy. "That's the third time you've been up there this morning."

"Well – er – well, I'm just looking down to make sure it isn't blocked up," said monkey, telling a lie. "You see, if the dolls ever wanted to light a fire and the chimney was blocked up in any way, it would smoke, and then their kitchen would become full of clouds of smoke and they wouldn't be able to breathe."

"But why should the chimney be

blocked up?" asked the sailor doll, surprised. "It never has been. It's never smoked when the dolls have lit a fire. Of course smoke comes out of the chimney, but what you mean is that if it were blocked up the smoke would puff down into the fireplace and into the room. But why should it be?"

"I don't know," said Monkey. "But there's no harm in keeping an eye on it, is there?"

"Well, if you like sitting on roofs and staring down chimneys for a silly reason like that, we can't stop you," said the sailor doll. "Would you like somebody to help you to keep an eye on the chimney? Someone might be silly enough."

"Oh, no. No, I can manage by myself," said Monkey, sliding down the roof and leaping to the ground. "I'm rather interested in chimneys, you know."

"I didn't know," said the sailor doll. "I've never thought that chimneys were so very interesting myself. Perhaps you are thinking of becoming a chimney-sweep, Monkey?"

Monkey didn't like being teased. He sat in a corner and sulked, waiting for a chance to go up on the roof of the doll's-house again and have a nibble at the biscuit. If only the toys would go off and play in a corner somewhere! They did at last, and Monkey sprang up to the roof again. Could he manage to have just a little nibble?

But no – the big doll had seen him, and she called the others and pointed at Monkey. "He's up there again! He's

chimney mad. Let's give him a chimney of his own when it's his birthday – one he can carry about with him!"

Now, the doll's-house dolls got worried when they heard that Monkey was keeping an eye on their chimney in case it got blocked up.

"Why should he think that?" they said. "Let's light a fire to show him that it's quite all right. He makes such a noise on the roof, jumping up and down. It's most disturbing."

So one night they lit a fire in the fireplace of their dear little house. The

toys always loved to see the fire in the doll's-house lit, it looked so cosy and friendly. The teddy, the sailor doll and the dolls went to peer in at the window. They were too big to walk in through the front door.

"It's alight," said Sammy. "I can hear it crackling – and now, see, there are the flames!"

"It looks nice," said the big doll. "I feel quite warm just looking at it!"

"But see – it's beginning to smoke!" said the teddy bear, in alarm. "It really is. Clouds of smoke are pouring down the chimney into the kitchen! There must be something in the chimney! Monkey was right – it *is* blocked up!"

Monkey ran up.

"Oh, don't light a fire!" he begged, thinking of his lovely biscuit hidden in the chimney. The smoke would spoil it, he was sure. "Please don't light a fire!"

"Monkey, you were right – the chimney is blocked up," said Sammy.

Then one of the doll's-house dolls gave a scream. "Help! Help! Something is streaming down the chimney and into the fireplace – oh, whatever is it?" Well, you can guess what it was, of course! The heat from the fire had melted the chocolate, and it was running down the chimney into the fireplace in a warm, sticky river!

"It's running all over the floor. What is it?" screamed the dolls.

The clockwork mouse, who could easily get in at the front door, ran in to help. He sniffed at the brown stream oozing down the chimney.

"Why – it's chocolate!" he said. "I know it is! I'll lick it and see!"

So he licked it and, of course, it was chocolate!

"But how could chocolate get into the chimney?" said the teddy bear, his nose pressed against the window outside. "What an extraordinary thing. Monkey, come here. Do you know anything about that chocolate?"

"He's gone as red as a tomato," said the big doll. "He knows all about it. Monkey – was it you who put it there?"

"Well," said the Monkey, "well, this is what happened. You see . . . ."

"What you really mean is that you found a chocolate or something on the floor and didn't want to share it and hid it in the chimney," said the big doll, who was very clever. "Mean old Monkey! And now the doll's-house dolls have lit a fire to find out if the chimney is blocked or not – and your chocolate has melted. Ha-ha! You won't get it now."

"It was a chocolate finger biscuit," said Monkey, mournfully. "It went down the chimney nicely. I wished I'd shared it now!"

"Well, the clockwork mouse and all the toy animals from the farm can lick the chocolate up," said Sammy. "It serves you right. You won't even get a nibble. And I don't really feel I want to talk to you for quite a long while, Monkey."

The farm animals and the clockwork mouse were delighted. What a feast! The big toys watched them through the doll's-house windows. All except Monkey, and he went and sat himself down with his face in a corner.

"Look – he's put himself in a corner," said Sammy, with a giggle.

"Good thing, too!" said Teddy, "I'd have put him there myself if I'd thought of it."

They forgave Monkey after a while, but whenever it seemed as if he was

going to be a bit mean again, they all began to talk loudly about chimneys. Then Monkey went red and stopped being selfish.

As for the biscuit part of the chocolate, that didn't melt, of course. It stayed in the chimney for quite a long while and then one day a real little mouse came into the playroom and sniffed it out and ate it.

A Pennyworth
of Kindness

Once George was on a bus going home, when a little girl got on and sat beside him. She felt in her pocket for her money, and then she looked very scared.

She sat quite still, and George wondered what was the matter. He soon knew, when the conductor came up. George gave him his money, and got his ticket – but the little girl began to cry.

"I must get out at the next stop," she told the conductor. "I must walk home, I haven't got my money in my pocket. I must have lost it."

"Now look here," said the conductor, who was a cross-looking fellow, "you're the third child who's told me that story today, and…"

"But I really have lost it," said the

little girl. "I've got a hole in my pocket."

"Look – I can pay your fare," said George, and he put some money into the little girl's hand. "My uncle gave me this yesterday, and you can have it."

"Oh, thank you!" said the little girl, and she gave it to the conductor, and he handed her a ticket. "You are kind. What's your name? I'll give it back to you when Mummy gives me my pocket money."

"My name's George," the little boy said. "But I don't want the money back.

You can have it. I've got some more at home."

"All the same, I shall pay you back for your pennyworth of kindness," said the little girl. That made George laugh. A pennyworth of kindness really sounded funny.

The little girl ran home to her mother, when she got out at her stop. She told her all about George and his kindness.

"Well, that's really nice of the boy," said her mother. "I wonder who he is, Mollie?"

But she couldn't find out, and Mollie never saw him on the bus again. She was worried about the money that she hadn't paid back.

"What shall I do, Mummy?" she said. "I must do something – and I've just had a birthday, so I've got lots of money."

"Well, dear, if you can't pay the bit of kindness back to George, you can always pay it to someone else who needs it," said her mother. "Look out for someone."

So Mollie looked out, and she soon found somebody. It was old Mrs Forrester.

Mollie saw her coming along the road, carrying a basket. Just as she came up to Mollie, the old lady slipped and fell, her basket fell too, and there was a little crashing sound.

"Oh dear, oh dear!" said Mrs Forrester, picking herself up. "There go my eggs! It's all right, Mollie, I haven't hurt myself – but I've cracked my precious eggs – and I've no money to go and buy more!"

"I've got some money! I'll buy you some more, Mrs Forrester!" cried Mollie, seeing that here was a chance for her to pay the bit of kindness she owed. She raced off to the farm, explained what had happened and bought four more eggs for fifty pence. She went to Mrs Forrester's house and gave them to her.

"No, no," said the old lady. "I can't take them, Mollie dear. You're too kind."

"I'm not," said Mollie. "I'm only paying back a pennyworth of kindness I got from a boy called George, but as I've got a lot of money just now, I've made it a fifty pence!"

"Fifty-pence-worth of kindness!" said Mrs Forrester, and she laughed. "What a funny idea – and what a good one! I owe you fifty-pence-worth of kindness, Mollie."

"You don't need to pay it back to me, you can easily pay it to somebody else, just as I've done," said Mollie.

Mrs Forrester quite meant to pay it back to Mollie, but she fell ill after that, and had no money to pay back anything to anyone. Her brother came to see her, and as he was both kind and well-off, he paid all her bills and took her off to his home.

"Do you owe any more money to anyone?" he asked his sister, as he put her into his car to take her away with him. "You are sure you have told me all your bills?"

"Well – I owe fifty-pence-worth of kindness to a little girl," said his sister in a weak voice, and she told her brother about Mollie. "I don't know where she lives – so you can't very well pay her back."

"Well, I can pay it to someone else instead," said her brother. "If you owe someone fifty-pence-worth of kindness I must certainly deal with it!"

He watched for a chance, but it didn't come for some time. Then he saw a little girl knocked off her bicycle by a car, and he ran to pick her up. He put her in his own car, and took her to the nearest doctor. She wasn't badly hurt, but she was very, very frightened.

The doctor soon bandaged her cut arm and leg, but Pamela still cried bitterly.

"I'll take you home now," said Mrs Forrester's brother. "And on the way we'll stop at a toyshop, and I'll buy you a great big doll – but you must stop crying if I do that!"

"You're very kind!" said Pamela, shyly.

"Ah, I have a bit of kindness to pay to somebody," said Mrs Forrester's brother, and he told Pamela all about how kind Mollie had been to his sister and about the bus-fare that George had given Mollie. "Well, here we are at the toyshop – and here's the very doll for you!"

He bought a beauty, and then drove Pamela home. He left her at the front door, and drove off, because he did not want to be thanked. Pamela went in and told her mother and father all that had happened. She showed them the beautiful doll.

"But who was this kind, generous fellow?" said her father. " Didn't you ask his name? I must find him and pay him back his great kindness to you."

But Pamela didn't know who had been so kind to her, and looked after her and given her the lovely doll. Her father tried his hardest to find out, but he couldn't.

Pamela was worried. "We ought to pay back his kindness somehow, Daddy, oughtn't we?" she said. "It all began with that pennyworth of kindness on the bus. That kind man told me the whole story – how a little boy paid a little girl's bus-fare, and when she found she couldn't pay it back, she bought this man's sister fifty-pence-worth of eggs, because hers got broken – so that was fifty-pence-worth of kindness – and the sister couldn't pay it back because she didn't know where the little girl lived, so the brother said…"

"Said he'd pay it back, but to somebody else!" said her mother. She turned to Pamela's father. "John! A pennyworth of kindness became fifty-pence-worth. The fifty-pence-worth has become ten-pounds-worth, because that is exactly what the kind fellow paid for this doll!"

"And I shall make it a hundred-pounds-worth!" said Pamela's father. "My little girl is very precious to me, and I would give a hundred pounds to anyone in return for helping her. If only I could find this fellow."

But he couldn't, so do you know what he did? He spent his hundred pounds on

buying new swings for the playground in the village, a new sand-pit for the children, too, and he even put in a lovely paddling-pool for the little ones.

George goes there every Saturday, with his sister Jane and his little brother Ian. Jane plays in the sand-pit, Ian plays in the paddling-pool, George plays with them both and goes on the swings. They have a really wonderful time.

George doesn't know that all these lovely playthings were put there because of his pennyworth of kindness. He just thinks that Pamela's father must be one of the kindest men in the world to give so many marvellous things to the children in the village.

How I'd love to give someone a pennyworth of kindness and see it grow and grow! Wouldn't you? Let's try it whenever we get the chance!

Pussy's
Ride

Kate and Robbie were most excited. Their father said he would take them to the city with him. He was going to London, and he said that for a treat the two children could go too. Then he would take them to the circus there, and they would all have a fine time!

Father bought the tickets at the station. They all got into a carriage when the train came in at their platform. The guard waved his flag – the train was off!

Robbie and Kate looked out of the window and saw trees and fields rushing by. Then the train slowed down and pulled into another station. A little girl with a big box got into the train. She looked at Kate and Robbie.

They looked at her. The box was funny,

because it had holes in every side of it! What a strange box!

"Where are you going?" Robbie asked the little girl.

"I am going to the city," said the little girl.

"What is inside your box?" said Kate.

"Aha!" said the little girl. "Wouldn't you like to know!"

"Do tell us!" said Robbie.

"It's my cat," said the little girl. "She is going to my granny who lives in London – and do you know, my granny is taking me to the circus this afternoon!"

"Oh! We are going too!" said Kate. "How funny!"

"Miaow! Miaow!" said Pussy, inside the box, and she scratched to try to get out. "Miaow!"

"The holes are to let air in so that she can breathe," said the little girl. "Mummy was afraid she would jump out and escape if I took her in a basket, so we put her in this special box. My granny is meeting me at the station. I am staying with her for three whole days. We have

three little kittens at home now, so Mummy said my granny could have Pussy for her own, because Granny has lots of mice in her house."

"Look out for us at the circus!" said Robbie, as the train pulled into the big station at London. "We will wave to you if we see you!"

They all got out. There was the little girl's granny waiting for her on the platform. How pleased she was! The little girl ran to her and kissed her.

And do you know, Robbie and Kate saw her again that afternoon! She was just in front of them at the circus, and they all waved to one another.

"Pussy has caught three mice already!" called the little girl. "She does love it at Granny's house!"

I wonder how many mice she has caught now, don't you? How many do you think?

The Toys and
the Goblins

Once upon a time, when the toys in the playroom were quietly playing hide-and-seek in the middle of the night, there came a small tap-tap-tapping at the window.

"What's that?" whispered the brown teddy bear, in a fright.

"Please, oh, please let us in!" cried a small voice. "We are the little blue fairies who live at the bottom of the garden. We have been chased by the big red goblin, and he will soon be after us again!"

Quickly the teddy bear and the sailor doll opened the window, and in climbed a troop of tiny blue fairies, all as pale as moonlight with fright.

"Goodness!" the sailor doll cried in astonishment. "Whatever can have happened to your lovely wings?"

"Oh, isn't it perfectly dreadful!" wept the first fairy. "The red goblin came while we were all sleeping the other night and cut all of our wings off!" She turned round and showed her clipped wings to the toys. "That goblin wants us all to be his servants, you know, for he has a big house up on the hillside, and he wants us to go and live there and keep it clean for him."

"But we have always said no," said another very small fairy.

"He is a nasty creature. He is terribly unkind, and so none of us fairies will have anything to do with him at all. We thought we would fly far away to our aunt, who lives up in the clouds, but before we could do that the horrible goblin came and cut our wings off."

"Yes," said the first fairy, wiping away her tears, "and if a big green frog hadn't happened to hop up and help us, then the goblin would have taken us all that very minute – but we managed to escape, by running away as fast as we could."

"Did he come after you again?" asked the sailor doll, looking very fierce.

"Oh, yes, he came again the very next night," said the tiny fairy. "We had hidden in the flower-bed but an unkind snail told him where we were and so he managed to hunt us out again. Then we hid ourselves under a mossy stone but he

159

managed to find us there as well – and tonight, just as we were sleeping in the hollow oak-tree, we heard him coming again – so we thought we would come to you for shelter."

"I'm very glad you did," said the big teddy bear, kindly. "You shall stay here with us as long as you like. There is plenty of room for you all in the toy-cupboard. If that nasty old goblin comes looking for you we'll soon frighten him off!"

"He said he would go and get twelve more goblins to help him come and fetch us," said the fairy. "Do you think you could manage to fight so many?"

The toys looked grave. The sailor doll shook his head.

"No," he said. "I don't think we could possibly fight so many goblins. You see we are only toys, and we're not very strong. But won't your wings grow back again, fairies?"

"Oh yes," said the little creatures, nodding their golden heads. "But not for a week or two. If only we could stay here

in safety for about a fortnight, our wings would grow properly again and we could spread them out and fly off to our aunt quite easily. Then the goblin couldn't possibly come and get us."

"Well, you must stay with us, then," said the bear. "We will keep a good look-out for the goblin, and if he does come with his friends we will save you somehow. We have a friend in the garden, a red-breasted robin. We will ask him to watch and see what the wicked goblin is doing, and if he comes to tell us that the goblins are all coming here to get you, we will hide you away safely somewhere."

161

So the blue fairies cheered up and were soon very happy. The toy train gave them a fine ride all round the playroom, and the big bus ran them to and fro on the rug till he nearly broke down!

Some of the fairies squeezed into the brick-box and the others found room in the doll's cot, when they were sleepy at cock-crow. The toys went back to their cupboard, and soon there was nothing to be seen or heard in the quiet playroom.

When the sun rose the robin came peeping in at the window. The sailor doll saw him and beckoned to him. The little bird flew into the room. Very soon the toys had told him all about the goblins and he promised to keep an eye on them and to tell the toys at once, if he heard that they were coming to the playroom. Off he flew, and the fairies heard him trilling a cheery little song in the tree outside.

Day after day went by and there was no sign of the red goblin. The robin came to see the toys each day and told them that everything was safe.

"The goblin is in his house on the hill," he sang. "He has not been to see any of the other goblins. Perhaps he has decided not to bother the blue fairies any more!"

The fairies were delighted. It was very pleasant living in the playroom. When Ann, the girl whose playroom it was,

came to play with the toys, the fairies often peeped out to watch. Ann had no idea at all that they were staying there, of course – but wouldn't she have been excited if she had seen them?

Each night the sailor doll turned the fairies round and looked at their clipped wings.

"Yes," he would say, his head on one side. "Yes, your wings are certainly growing fast again! They are bigger than they were last night. In a few days you all will be able to fly away safely to your aunt's house up in the clouds, and you won't have to worry about the goblin again!"

In a little while both toys and fairies began to forget the red goblin, for the robin never had any news of him. They felt quite sure that he had given up all hope of catching the fairies, and nobody worried any more.

So it was a dreadful shock to hear the robin singing in alarm one morning at sunrise. His voice was loud and he tapped at the windowpane.

164

"The goblin is coming tonight, tonight!" he sang. "He has twelve friends coming to help him! Yes, he has, he has! He sent them all a letter, and now they have promised to help him this very evening. What will you do, what will you do? Are the fairies' wings grown yet?"

"No, no!" cried the sailor doll in fright, and he pushed up the window to let in the robin. "They are too small for the fairies to fly with yet, they are only half the size they should be. It takes two weeks for wings to grow again. Oh my, oh my, whatever are we to do?"

165

The fairies began to cry, for they felt very frightened. "Oh, please, do think of some plan to help us!" they begged the toys. "You are so clever, so wise!"

Just then the toys heard a door opening downstairs and they knew it was Mother, who was up and ready to air the rooms and make the breakfast. So they scurried back to the toy-cupboard with the fairies, feeling frightened and worried. Whatever were they going to

do? The goblins would be sure to come that very night – and how were they going to save the poor little fairies? If only they could get them away to their aunt who lived up in the clouds! Then they would be quite safe from the goblin and his twelve friends.

All that day the toys thought and thought. The sailor doll frowned – the teddy bear groaned. What could they do?

Ann played with them as usual, but they couldn't even feel happy when they were with her. At last she put them down and opened a box she had found at the back of the cupboard.

Inside it there was a little pipe and some soapy liquid – it was a bubble-blowing set.

"This will be fun!" said Ann. "I'll blow some bubbles for a change!" So she dipped her pipe in the liquid and began to blow some beautiful big bubbles, which floated away through the open window and into the sunshine.

The toys watched in wonder – it really was a most beautiful sight.

167

And then the sailor doll had a marvellous idea – so marvellous that he could hardly wait for the night to come to tell the others. But at last the playroom was in darkness except for the moonlight that streamed in through the window, and the sailor doll hurriedly called the toys and fairies round him.

"I know how to save the fairies from the goblins!" he cried. "Did you see Ann blowing those lovely bubbles? Well, why don't we blow some too, and each of the tiny fairies can slip inside a bubble and be blown out of the window and right up to the clouds! Then they will all be quite safe!"

"What a wonderful idea!" cried everyone, and the fairies shouted in delight. So the sailor doll went to the cupboard and got out the bubble box.

Just at that moment the robin tapped on the window. "The goblins are coming, the goblins are coming!" he trilled. "I kept awake tonight to see – and I have just spied a big crowd of them creeping up the garden."

The blue fairies began to cry. The teddy bear comforted them and told the sailor doll to hurry up as much as he possibly could. The sailor doll at once began to blow bubbles. You should have seen them! He blew beautiful big ones, all shining and glittering and, as he blew each one, one of the tiny little fairies slipped inside and waited for the bubble to get bigger.

Then the teddy bear blew it off the pipe and all the toys puffed and puffed till the bubble floated out of the window and up into the sky.

"Once we are at our aunt's we shall be safe!" cried the fairies. "Goodbye, dear toys! Goodbye, all of you, and thank you for all your kindness. We'll come and see you again when our wings have grown."

Just then there came some loud shouts and growls and into the room swarmed a crowd of red goblins, with wicked, shining eyes and long, pointed ears. They shook their fists at the toys and cried, "Where are all those fairies? Where have you hidden them? Tell us at once, or it will be the worse for you!"

Only two small blue fairies were left by now. All the others had safely floated off in the bubbles. The toys quickly stood in front of the two fairies, and the sailor doll went on blowing bubbles quite calmly.

The goblins climbed into the playroom and ran to the toy-cupboard to hunt for the fairies. The sailor doll blew a big

bubble and one of the two fairies slipped inside it. Off she went, floating through the window and up into the air. Then the sailor doll blew another bubble and the last fairy squeezed into it. He blew it bigger, and the bear puffed it off the bowl of the pipe. It rose towards the window and all the toys blew hard. It floated out and up into the air – and just at that very moment the goblins saw the fairy inside it!

How they shouted! How they yelled! How they shook their fists! But it wasn't a bit of good – the little blue fairies were all gone, every single one. They had all escaped safely!

All the noise woke up Ann, who was asleep in her bedroom nearby. She sat up in bed and listened. There certainly was a noise! The goblins were attacking the toys, who were trying to fight back, but dear me, the goblins were far too fierce for them!

Just as the goblins were about to take the frightened toys prisoner, Ann came pattering to the door. At once the goblins

fled out of the window, and the toys rushed back to the toy-cupboard. Ann found no one about – but to her surprise, there, in the middle of the table was her bubble set, with the pipe still in the bubble liquid!

She was astonished! "Now who in the world has been playing with that?" she wondered. "How strange! I should love to know."

But nobody ever told her – though if she had listened very carefully to the robin's song that winter she might have heard the whole story, Anyway, that's how I got to know all about it!

The Cross
Old Man

Dan and Daisy were staying at the seaside. It was lovely. The sky was blue, the sun was hot, the sea was as blue as the sky.

The twins paddled in the sea and dug in the sand and bathed all day long. They played with the other children and built some very fine sandcastles with lovely, big moats.

One afternoon, when the children were building a fort out of the sand, Dan looked down the beach towards the sea to find out whether the tide was coming in. They wanted to finish building the fort before the sea came right up and washed it away.

"Oh look – the tide is coming in – and it's almost reached right up to the feet of that old man," said Dan. "Do you suppose he knows? Look, the man in the deckchair over there, I mean!"

"Well, he's looking out to sea, so I suppose he can see the tide coming in!" said Janet. "And anyway, he's a horrid old man. He's always cross and shouting."

The tide crept right up to the old man's feet. Dan was surprised that he didn't move. He ran down and had a good look at him.

"He's asleep!" he said to the others. "I do think we ought to wake him."

"Well, when my dog barked and woke him up on the beach yesterday he was very cross. He shouted at me and then he threw a stone at my poor dog," said Jim.

"That was very mean of him," said Daisy. "No, don't wake him up, Dan. Let him stay there and get wet."

"No, we can't do that," said Dan. "You know what Mum always says – if people do nasty things to you, it is no reason why you should do nasty things to them. I think I am going to wake him up – even if he does shout at me for doing it!"

176

So Dan went to wake the old man. He touched him gently on the arm.

"Wake up, sir! The tide is coming in."

The old man woke up.

"Dear me! So it is! What a very kind little boy you are! Thank you!"

And do you know what the old man did? He bought ice creams for every one of the children on the beach who were building the fort! What a lovely surprise that was! He wasn't such a cross old man after all! Dan was so glad he had woken him up.

The
Disappointed Sprites

Once upon a time the little water sprites were very sad. They sat swinging in the rushes that grew by the side of the lake, and talked about their trouble.

"I don't think it's fair!" said Willow. "Why shouldn't we water sprites be allowed to dance in the fairy ring too? I do think that the fairies are mean!"

"Is it really true that they said we weren't to dance with them any more?" asked Trickle.

"Yes, it's true. Didn't you know?" said Splashabout. "They sent us a letter this morning. Read it out to us, Willow."

Willow took a letter from her pocket and spread it out. "This is what they say," she began. "Dear Water Sprites: Please do not come and dance in our

179

fairy ring any more. You spoil our dances. With love from the Fairies."

"Well! How very horrible of them!" cried Trickle. "Why don't they want us any more? We behave quite nicely!"

"Let's go and ask them!" said Splashabout. "And if we think their reason is fair, we won't make a fuss. But if it isn't, we'll go and complain to the Queen."

So the little sprites set off over the grass to Pixie Town among the toadstools. Here were fairies and elves, pixies and brownies. They all stared at the three sprites as they came running up, and wondered what was the matter.

"What do you want?" they cried. "Have you lost something?"

"No," answered Willow, "but we want to know why we aren't allowed to come and dance with you any more. What have we done to upset you?"

"Nothing," said a fairy. "It isn't really your fault."

"Well, whose fault is it, then?" asked Splashabout, impatiently. "We think it really is very, very mean of you."

180

The pixies and fairies looked at each other. Nobody wanted to explain. At last a brownie broke the silence.

"It's like this," he said. "You're always so wet, and when we dance with you we spoil our clothes."

"And you make all the seats wet too, with your damp frocks," said an elf.

"And I've got a dreadful cold through putting on one of your wet shawls by mistake. A-tishoo! A-tishoo!" said a pixie, and blew his nose loudly.

The water sprites stared sadly at the fairies.

"But we can't help being wet," said Trickle, sorrowfully. "We live in the water, you see, so we're always wet and we never, ever get colds."

"That's because you're used to it," said a fairy. "We aren't, and we feel as if we're dancing with frogs when we dance with you. We're awfully sorry about it, but you do spoil all our dances."

The water sprites looked at each other, and decided to be brave about it.

"We're sorry," said Willow. "We quite understand."

"But it is dreadfully disappointing, because we do so like dancing," said Trickle, nearly bursting into tears.

"And there's no place on the water where we can dance," said Splashabout.

Then they said goodbye and went sadly back to the lake. They told all the water sprites what they had heard, and everyone was very upset.

"That's the end of all our dancing," said Ripple. "It's a great pity, for we are the lightest and daintiest of all fairy folk."

"Well, we must just make the best of it," said Willow. "We'll go and watch next time the fairies have a dance, but we won't go near enough to wet them."

So next time the elves and fairies held a dance in the fairy ring, the sprites crept up to watch them. They heard the music played by the grasshoppers and bees, and longed to join in the dance, but they had made up their minds to be good – and so they were.

Carefully they hid themselves in the long grass around the fairy ring and peeped out from behind the wild flowers to watch quietly.

Now, it happened that the Fairy Queen decided to go to the dance that night. She floated down, pale and beautiful in the moonlight, and took her place on the little silver throne that always stood waiting for her.

The fairies were delighted to see her, and made a great fuss of her for she was very good to them. "Go on with your dancing," she said. "I love to watch you."

So they all danced and tripped, and pranced and skipped, as merry as could be, till suddenly the Queen wondered where the water sprites were. They had never missed a dance before, and she couldn't think why they weren't there. She peeped all round the dancers, but not one sprite could she see.

And then she suddenly spied them peeping and peering behind the buttercups and daisies outside the fairy ring! She was astonished!

She clapped her hands and ordered the dance to stop for a minute. Everyone turned to hear what Her Majesty had to say.

"Why do the water sprites peep and hide, instead of dancing?" she asked. "Have they been naughty?"

"Oh no, Your Majesty!" answered a pixie. "They're not at all naughty. We sent them a letter asking them not to come to our dances any more."

"Why did you do that?" asked the Queen in astonishment.

"Because they are always so dreadfully

185

wet!" answered the pixie. "They ruin our clothes and make us catch terrible colds."

"But haven't they anywhere to dance now?" asked the Queen.

"No, nowhere," said the pixie. "They can't dance on the lake, you see, and we can't have them in our dancing rings any more."

"Dear, dear!" said the Queen. "Whatever can we do! Were the water sprites nice about it, or were they angry?"

"They were ever so nice," said all the fairies at once.

"They promised not to come!" said a brownie.

"And they said they were sorry and they quite understood!" called an elf.

The Queen was pleased. She liked to hear of people taking disappointment cheerfully. She waved her hand.

"Go on with your dancing," she said, looking thoughtful.

The bees and grasshoppers began playing again, and the fairies took their partners and went merrily on with their dance.

They didn't see the Queen slip away through the grass. She went very quietly, her crown gleaming like dewdrops in the bright moonlight.

She went to the lake. It lay very peaceful and still. All the sprites who usually played there were away watching the dance.

Big white and yellow waterlilies lay on the water. The Queen called to them.

"Waterlilies," she cried, "where are your leaves?"

"Down in the water!" answered the waterlilies in voices like a hundred singing ripples.

"Listen!" said the Queen. "Raise them to the top of the lake, and let them spread themselves smooth and flat on the water."

The waterlilies all raised their leaves and did as they were told. Gradually the lake became spread with big flat leaves, shining in the moonlight.

"Thank you," said the Queen. "You look beautiful now, waterlilies. Will you let the little water sprites dance on your leaves when the lake is calm?"

"Yes! Yes!" sang the waterlilies softly. "We love the water sprites; they look after our buds for us!"

Then the Queen called the green frogs to her, and told each one to fetch his instrument and climb on to the waterlily leaves and play a merry tune.

"Yes, Your Majesty!" they cried, and quickly clambered up. Then they struck

up such a loud, merry tune that all the fairies and sprites away by the dancing ring listened in astonishment. Then they all ran helter-skelter to the lake to see what the music could be.

There they found the Queen, sitting on a waterlily, with the frogs playing their instruments as merrily as could be.

"Look! Look!" cried the fairies. "The waterlilies have brought their leaves to the surface!"

"What fun! What fun!" cried the water sprites, jumping on to the leaves. "Oh, Your Majesty, we could dance on these leaves! May we?"

"Yes, you may," answered the Queen, smiling. "And now, whenever the fairies hold a dance in the fairy ring, you may hold a dance on the waterlily leaves, for the frogs will play for you until dawn!"

"Oh, thank you, thank you!" cried the sprites in great delight. They each took a partner and were soon happily dancing on the smooth waterlily leaves, while the fairies looked on in wonder.

When dawn came, nothing was to be seen of the Queen or the fairies. The water sprites were gone, and so were the frogs and their instruments.

But calm and steady the waterlily leaves floated on the water, waiting for the time when little feet should dance on them once again.

Look at them, next time you pass by a

lake. The biggest leaf you see is the one that all the frogs stand on to play their instruments, and the biggest waterlily is the one the Queen sits on. Don't you think it was a splendid idea of hers?